DRIFTWOOD PRESS

EDITORS

JAMES MCNULTY
MANAGING FICTION EDITOR
VISUAL ARTS EDITOR
MAGAZINE DESIGNER
COPYEDITOR

DAN LEACH
FICTION EDITOR

FELICIA KROL
FICTION EDITOR

CLAIRE AGNES
FICTION EDITOR

STEPHEN HUNDLEY
FICTION EDITOR

SHANE PAGE
GUEST FICTION EDITOR

SUSAN JARDANEH
GUEST FICTION EDITOR

MEGAN SWENSON
GUEST FICTION EDITOR

JERROD SCHWARZ
MANAGING POETRY EDITOR
VISUAL ARTS EDITOR

CREDITS

Independently published by *Driftwood Press*
in the United States of America.

Fonts: Satellite, Garamond, Cinzel, League Gothic,
& Merriweather.
Cover Image & Content Illustrations: Coz Frimpong
Cover Design: Sally Franckowiak
Magazine Design: James McNulty
© Driftwood Press, 2020
All Rights Reserved.

Published in July 2020
ISSN Print: 2578-7195
ISSN Online: 2331-7132
ISBN-13: 978-1-949065-07-7

Please visit our website at www.driftwoodpress.net
or email us at editor@driftwoodpress.net.

ISSUE 7.2

TABLE OF

1 & 6
JESSICA HOLBERT
TRASH MAN
~
INTERVIEW

19 & 25
SETH BRADY TUCKER
THE TAXIDERMIST
~
INTERVIEW

34, 36, 38, & 40
GEOFFREY DETRANI
ANGEL OF HISTORY
RENDITION GARDEN
STALEMATE COSMOLOGY
TROPHIES TREATIES

43 & 44
ANNIE CHRISTAIN
EVERY TIME I GO BACK IS
ENCODED IN PI
~
INTERVIEW

46 & 47
EMILY PAIGE WILSON
APPROPRIATE JEWELS
FOR COURTSHIP
~
INTERVIEW

48 & 50
KAY LIN
DISASSOCIATION
~
INTERVIEW

52 & 53
CHELSEA JACKSON
GAIA
~
INTERVIEW

55 & 56
JANIRU LIYANAGE
AFTER AIDEN DIES HALFWAY
THROUGH CHEMO
~
INTERVIEW

58 & 59
JOHN DAVIS JR.
LAWN BODIES
~
INTERVIEW

CONTENTS

60 & 61
WREN TUATHA
BLENDER
~
INTERVIEW

62 & 63
TURANDOT SHAYEGAN
AMERICA BABY
~
INTERVIEW

64 & 65
JOANNA LEE
BRUISES FROM GOD
~
INTERVIEW

66 & 67
KATHERINE FALLON
LANDMINE
~
INTERVIEW

68 & 69
MADELEINE FRANK
THE LIGHTNING BOX ON THE
EDGE OF BOYKIN CREEK
~
INTERVIEW

70 & 71
MOLLY OBERSTEIN-ALLEN
THE PORT BEGAT THE STORM
~
INTERVIEW

72
AIMEE COZZA
THE WICKED WOODS

74 & 75
YI-HUI HUANG
UNTITLED
UNTITLED

76 & 84
JASON HART
COMPLEXIO
~
INTERVIEW

TRASH MAN

JESSICA HOLBERT

Before Trash Man's name was Trash Man he was Bill Temper. When the garbage trucks stopped coming he took our waste and let it pile high on his front lawn. But no one remembers that. Hell, even I forgot until recently.

Trash Man lived in a one-story ranch. A single streetlamp stood out front. Even during the day it ticked on and off. The carousel sat in the yard, which Trash Man had purchased cheap from the maintenance head of a nomadic fun park that'd been in town and left too early. The wattage to support the thing was too much for Trash Man's electric bill, and besides, some internal mechanism was busted. It didn't work on its own. My sister Corinne and I would cut through the neighbor's yard, wrap around their above-ground pool, to get to Trash Man's. His son Rory liked to be outside. He planted flowers inside the old Michelins from his father's deceased Bronco. Sometimes we caught him spitting on anthills. He'd see us and Corrine would wave. And then he'd understand and go inside and Trash Man would come out all smiles. He helped us on the porcelain horses, my favorite being a big colt with a crown of plastic holly on its head. Corinne preferred the mare with a fractured ear. She named it Star.

Even without electricity, Trash Man made the carousel work. He wound a rope around the central pillar and would say, "Ready, set!" and then pull it until his teeth gritted and we went around. All the other horses had broken seats because the rig that dumped it in the yard nearly saw it was toppled. So Rory took turns with us or sometimes sat in the saddle behind Corinne because he could fit.

Word was that Trash Man was gay, which was why Mrs. Temper left the poor bastard. At school, my classmates called him a faggot. Corinne and I once went to Mom and Dad asking about the orange Lincoln that came and left during odd hours of the night, blinking underneath that single broken streetlamp.

"Not any of our business," Mom said and went on shucking too much corn for that night's neighborhood barbecue. Dad stared. Out the window a collared housecat batted around a bird that had been pecking too long at the base of the feeder. Our father was terminally laconic and as he aged he seemed more content with it. Then that night, at the barbecue, Trash Man called us Honeycubs while he roasted a frankfurter in the fire pit, and we were sorry.

By this time Corinne and I had made arts-and-crafts kites out of wire hangers and old curtains. We "flew" them together with Rory down at Old Goose Pond. At school we said, "Sup, fella," to each other in the halls and traded the fruit in our lunch boxes. When Rory wasn't around, Corinne still let me into her bedroom. She painted her fingernails with ladybug spots and said things like, "Mom's been making me talk to Dad for her again."

Then the crisis started and everyone had bigger things to worry about.

One Thursday the garbage truck didn't come and so giant plastic bins stewed in driveways for a week. And then, next Thursday it still didn't come. And the next. Each school day Corinne and I found more bags at the end of our driveway, ants and ants crawling over escaped coffee grounds. From atop her balcony old Mrs. Leeks megaphoned that the sanitation department had forgotten us all and therefore so had God.

We weren't genuinely concerned until one sunset evening when the Georges tried to burn their undesireables and their porch caught fire. At the time of the accident Corinne, Rory, and I rode on the carousel, watching the smoke billow into the clouds from three streets over. The Georges ended up losing their garage and their three-week-old kitten who was trampled underneath Mrs. George as she screamed and held her head, an episode that later led to a diagnosis of PTSD. That evening, it was Mom who told us what had happened at the George fire. No longer sheltering us from an imperfect world, she knelt down in her pencil skirt and tugged our earlobes lovingly as she explained every detail. Dad stood buttoning and unbuttoning his flannel.

It got bad. Dog walkers pinched their noses down the street until they finally resolved to leave their dog's shit in their own yards. Drivers rolled up their windows and stuffed their a/c vents with rags. The only way to keep any sort of dignity was to double-bag, but eventually it all tore anyway. It was the weather, raccoons, unidentified junk hunters. Greening foodstuffs and BK bags and used kitty litter avalanched into the streets and piled tall up the posts of mailboxes.

Some nights I followed Corrine into the hall to the kitchen threshold. Once, we were in middle school and it was past our bedtime. She smelled of a fresh shower and I watched the mole on the back of her neck as we listened to Mom.

"I don't deserve this BS every night. Learn to sew your own buttons back on."

"What the hell, where are you going?"

"David, I'm already gone," Mom said, and Corrine's hand felt like warm putty.

We had the neighborhood meeting at the circle at the end of Little Summer Ave. Squirrels tight-roped along telephone wires. Pine needles eked out onto the pavement. Everyone walked there except one single mother who rolled up in her red pickup with her pimple-faced son. Not ten minutes in, someone ripped the jade pendant from their own aunt's turkey neck and then everybody was shouting. Dad chewed gum and let his fingers twist the buttons from his shirt.

That's when Trash Man became Trash Man. He vaulted on top of the red pickup and whistled like a hawk. Infants laughed and the pimple-faced boy craned his head out the window and said, "Fuck yeah." Trash Man's speech was short. We all clapped for his sacrifice and dozens of hands offered to help him off the truck's hood.

"Your Dad's good," I heard Corinne say to Rory.

Rory picked his nose, wiped it on the heel of his Sketchers.

Before the summer could come full-on to amplify the stench, we were saved. When people came to dump their bags at his house, Trash Man stood by his mailbox with his knuckles stuffed into his cargoes. He once offered my father a cold one when he'd come to dump a bundle of flattened-out cardboard boxes. At school, the beautiful daughter of the administration superintendent touched Rory's shoulders during lunch. The school band let him pick the opener for a spring concert. Corinne said he was unhappy. I said he was the happiest kid who ever had that much garbage in his lawn.

The mounds in Trash Man's yard toppled from sheer height. Our grass grew green.

Freshman year of high school I got a gig at Stop & Shop trying to sell Gazettes by looking customers in the eye and making them feel a little guilty. Meantime, Corinne was thinking about cosmetology. I came in her room one night to borrow her History textbook. Even though I could see it in her unzipped book bag, she told me she didn't have it. I said, "Why don't you stop being a bitch," and she stopped combing the hair of a dummy head she'd gotten from Mrs. Vee in the Tech Program. Mom had heard the vanity mirror smash and came in to pull us apart. I had bloody nail marks in my shoulders but I walked away with a clump of her hair in my hand plus one of her pink scrunchies.

By now Dad was getting old. Sometimes he came home from Trash Man's and said that the guy should start a pick-up service. But then he'd apologize aloud and to no one. We couldn't see Trash Man's ranch anymore, just the streetlamp out front. Also, people stopped bagging. They tossed Big Gulps and plastic water bottles and laceless shoes and dusty magazines from their car windows into the lawn. They came with boxes and upturned them on the driveway. Handleless hammers, halved towel racks, iodized pipes and gears and loose screws. Trash Man shoveled it best he could, but the constant redistribution of the trash throughout his lawn gave him spinal problems. His skin sagged and his eyes glazed over with glaucoma and he hobbled from mound to mound, each taller than him. Rory came to school smelling like ancient omelet. Once, Guidance paged him in to say he had to bathe more often. He returned to PE and then broke down when it was his turn at bat. In the north wing, I found Corinne rubbing his back while he slouched against a locker.

"It's not right," she whispered to him.

"A person can't survive on pity alone," I said as I walked by. I'd read that line in a novel from English class.

At dinner that night I left the table for a piss and saw Corinne by the front door laying tacks in my shoes. Sunsets were pink. In the winter the sun washed the clouds gray and then white.

Occasionally, people came from outside the neighborhood. Friends and relatives and sad peripatetic salesmen. They all asked about the supposed house in the landfill and were told that Trash Man hoarded trash. He lived for it. Even I had forgotten he'd offered to take upon the entire neighborhood's burden of waste.

Then one day Dad came home early from his job at the insurance company and had Corinne and I sit with him at the kitchen table for almost an hour. I watched the soil of our centerpiece bamboo plant grow dry and stay dry.

Dad didn't say a word. Corinne's flip flop dangled by its toe thong. My chair pressured the bones in my ass.

Dad's head was in his hands until Mom came home with a bag of clearance-sale cardigans looped over her shoulder. She said, guess how good she was going to look at the next barbecue and that she was sorry Mrs. George, with her PTSD, wasn't going to be there to see. Poor thing, she still had the night terrors.

"Don't tell me I deserve to find stuff like this," Dad said, holding up a letter we'd never seen before. Mom said maybe she should put her stuff down. "You told me you were going to end it with this guy."

"We're not talking about this in front of the kids."

"Why the hell shouldn't they listen?"

"Because I don't know where it's going to go."

So we did go. Just outside Laura Hendresson watered her lilacs and waved to us as she said, "Do you hear the thrushes calling?" At Old Goose Pond, teenage boys cast their lines to catch sun fish and then sent them back. We could smell Trash Man's house and we gravitated toward it. I asked Corinne if she remembered the carousel. She nodded and I looked at her neck mole as we went the rest of the way in silence.

Decaying rubbish had turned into liquefied mush, sopped over the lawn so that grass or weeds would never grow. We stopped under the broken streetlamp. Moths and mosquitoes circled about in the flashing pool of orange light. If the carousel was there, I didn't see it.

Trash Man pointed around the yard while Rory shoveled plastic bags caught in a nebulous of gunk. Then he threw the shovel down and screamed. Trash Man, bent-backed and stumbling over a noisy pile of aluminum cans, raised his hand and struck him. We heard Trash Man say, "You're going to have to do this one day."

By the time we got home, Dad's Ford wasn't in the driveway and we found Mom on the sofa with a glass of wine in her hand. She invited us to sit down and watch Bridezillas. During a commercial Corinne said she loved this show and I left to study vocab for the SATs.

A week later Mom left with only a single traveling suitcase. Dad peeled carrots over the sink while Corinne said goodbye in the driveway.

"Mom's a whore," I said to him.

He said, don't talk about your mother like that and go out and say goodbye. When I didn't move, he slammed his fist on the counter and the microwave beeped. I did as he said.

In a year Corinne would go to the mailbox and come back with a postcard from North Carolina. There was a quiet, cloudless sky and the precipice of a cliff. In the bottom left corner the cameraperson's shadow entered the frame. Corinne started to read the script and I told her to tell someone who cares.

"Mom wasn't happy with him," she said.

Just then Dad came from the kitchen with a box of mac in his hand. Milk dripped from his beard, which had now begun to gray. He asked if he could see the card and Corinne rolled her eyes and tucked it in her jeans. The last time I saw the postcard Corinne was showing it to Rory in his lawn and they were both standing next to an unwanted box of children's dolls. Her shoulders shook and Rory had his hand around her waist.

At Trash Man's there had been a few scares that made the newspaper. By now I'd had my shitty Gazette job for three years, looking less pitiable with facial hair. I passed the time by reading and rereading the stories. The most severe involved the viscous swampland—it had been forming in Trash Man's yard for years—and an eight-year-old girl. Apparently she'd wandered over chasing a hare or toad or butterfly—it wasn't clear. But she soon found herself ankle- and then knee-deep in a composite mixture of muck, oil, kerosene, and God knows what. The girl screamed her head off until a babysitter from across the street was interested enough to come out and look. She found the girl up to her neck in sludge and wretched her out by having her grab hold of a deflated inner tube. The babysitter was famous for a week and when she went around the neighborhood with Professional Child Saver on her resume no one called it hubris. And so from then on everyone told their kids to stay away from Trash Man's.

As a result there were only four mourners at Trash Man's funeral some months later. Me, old Mrs. Leeks, Rory, and Corinne. Chalked up to heart failure. He died peacefully in his sleep. In front of the grave Rory choked over his words and tried to say that he didn't hear his father stir the night he died. He would have because he, Rory, liked to watch Bad Girls Club on mute. I drove us all back to Pond Shores after the service. Mrs. Leeks, the megaphone lady, rode shotgun and Corinne and Rory sat in the back.

"I'll tell yas," Mrs. Leeks said, "the man was a saint. A real saint." She wore a black skirt filigreed with yellow floral pattern. She kept apologizing for it but said it was the best mourning clothes she had. "Worn these to Mr. Leeks' funeral, too. Yeller was his favorite color though."

In the rearview, I watched Rory cry on Corinne's shoulder while she fixed the orchid pinned to his lapel. She kept whispering that it was alright, that everything was alright, that even Bill was alright.

Most nights I thought about Rory and how much I hated him, the nights I knew Corinne wasn't home. That kept happening until it was permanent. I had come home from buying Dad his gluten-free groceries and half of Corinne's bedroom was piled up in boxes on the living room floor. She pulled at the collar of her V-neck and smelled like the last of our pumpkin spice body wash.

"Taking after Mom," I said.

"Mom's a thousand miles away," she said. "I'll be down the street."

I always thought that Dad was so terse because everything was already being said. Maybe he just didn't know what to say.

"What about your other stuff?" I tried.

"Leave it," she said. "It's all trash." As she picked up a box, she said, "Oh. I guess I'll take it anyway."

I didn't sleep. During the days I readjusted Dad's oxygen tubes and made sure his wheelchair didn't run them over. He said things to me now like, "Thanks, buddy" and "Won't be for much longer."

Sometimes I talked about Mom in between TV commercials because I got the idea that he liked it, that time did actually heal old wounds. I made things up. She sent me messages on Facebook. At work (I had taken a job at an Enterprise post-graduation), I received mailed coffeecakes and Edible Arrangements.

And then one day he stopped eating his protein bar. Flakes of granola that had caught in his beard fell onto his bare stomach and cartwheeled into his bellybutton. His eyes welled and he told me that I should stop. I said, "Yeah," and went to toss an apple core and seethed over a full trash bin. In the days after she moved out, Corinne started working sixty a week at Shut Up & Dye. I still thought about Rory, how much I regretted going to his father's funeral. So I left the house, without the trash bag, and found Rory mulling over a blood-stained Tempurpedic, saying, "Who would throw this out?"

I grabbed him by the collar and one of his buttons popped. We stumbled and he said, "Don't hit me don't hit me," and I told him to shut the hell up. Then we toppled over together onto the bed. The sky was screaming yellow and the sun broke the clouds into a million pieces.

"Don't take my sister away from me," I said in tears.

"Can't I have anything, anything?" he said back.

He started to die, to bleed. I didn't remember hitting him, didn't remember him being hit. Then the world zeroed in and I realized that the blood I saw was the blood on the mattress, under his head like a crazy red halo.

So yesterday Corinne says this to me: "You're my brother, so what is wrong with you?"

We're in the living room and she's tall and her teeth are white and she's got a cowlick that wiggles under the blades of the ceiling fan. She's come to take the rest of what was unwanted in her bedroom. Light spangles through the blinds, onto the sofa. Dad is asleep in his wheelchair and the TV murmurs used-auto commercials. Every once in a while he grunts himself awake, sucks his saliva, and falls back asleep.

We're standing there for minutes. We watch the same thing. Us as kids, playing in the memories of our past. Our child selves peek around corners and giggle and then run because they're afraid and excited and happy to see that this is what they have become. Two siblings in the same room. We're about to continue living. We're about to be uncoiled from the caverns of our hearts. Now, my sister tells me that everything is, even I am, alright. And I can't stop noticing that I love her.

"You know that I don't pity Rory," she says. "I don't honor him either. That's not why."

"Why is it then?" I say.

And for my whole life I watch her not answer.

She only hugs me and goes out the screen door to where Rory is waiting in his graying Tacoma. In its bed there are old TVs without remotes, three-legged tables, rusted kitchen utensils; he's started a pick-up service. They go back to their home, Rory and my sister, behind all the garbage, its peaks and its valleys. And then I think, digging through the mounds of years and years of trash until I get deep inside, until I remember:

Trash Man whose name had been Bill Temper—there he is, just after he's pulled the rope on the carousel. The sun beats wrinkles into his forehead, and as we three pass in our rotations his hand is up: he's waving and then he's shading his brow and then he's waving at us again. And we're thinking that his pull has been strong enough so that we'll never stop: the trees and the ranch and Bill will keep spinning forever. For a frozen infinity, it never does stop. We would laugh and laugh and go round and round.

HURT & HEAL

A CONVERSATION WITH
JESSICA HOLBERT

The following conversation was conducted by managing fiction editor James McNulty.

James McNulty: Welcome back to the *Driftwood* family, Jessica! Congratulations on winning the 2020 In-House Short Story Contest! This is the first time *Driftwood* will publish a second story by the same fiction writer; I remember we published "Birch, Bark" in issue 3.1 (2016), albeit under a different name. It's been a while since I've read "Birch, Bark," but I think "Trash Man" is an even more successful story—and all our editors were thrilled by it. How've you been since?

Jessica Holbert: Thank you so much, it's always a good feeling to find a home for a story. Glad to be back!

As the name change would suggest, I've been rather busy attuning myself to a new gender identity. It's been challenging but also deeply rewarding. Every one of my relationships—be it with family, friends, or coworkers—has been enhanced for the better. But that's not really where it ends because it's sort of carried over into my writing as well. I can't help thinking of this one moment I shared with my step mother. She'd read a story of mine when I was a young writer and told me she really liked it. However, now all I had to do was "find my own voice." I labored over that criticism for a while to the point where I thought of it after every story I wrote. And that's where my stories remained most of the time, somewhere on the plane of voicelessness. The thing is, you can't have a voice, at least a real and honest voice, in your story unless you are honest within yourself. Stories are just too intimate to do anything but reveal some kind of significant truth. Not only for the reader but also the writer. Now that I'm out to myself and the rest of the world, I feel that I can produce stories that have a genuine voice. And I'm super happy that transitioning has helped bring that about.

JM: Interesting! Let's delve further into that, if you don't mind. You talk about "finding your voice." What does this mean to you, exactly? Does "your own voice" come through in the phrasing? The sentence structure? The character voice? The topic and theme choices? All of these?

Of course, this phrase makes its rounds a ton with young writers; we think of extremely distinctive voices like George Saunders, Ernest Hemingway, Virginia Woolf—writers who you can guess just from reading a few lines. But of course, not all writers are quite so distinctive in their "voice" as other writers, and that's okay. It's always felt to me like a lot of pressure to put on thousands of young writers to "find their own distinctive voice." Also, the attempt to try hard to find a voice seems to me inauthentic due to the nature of trying to force something; that is to say, it's hard to be "authentic" if you're trying to force something.

JH: Right so, I totally see why it's almost antagonistic to order a young a writer to find their voice. The whole discovery process does have to come out organically if a voice is to be truly authentic. In addition to phrasing, sentence structure, characters, etc, you have to put in work outside the margins. Meaning personal experience. Think about why we look to writers, and artists at large, to tell us about the world, who or what is admirable, what's important, what makes us human. Crappy as it sounds, the earth would still turn without the help of artists. Engineers, scientists, doctors: not so much. Yet, we go to authors like Saunders and Hemingway and Woolf for some kind of sense of total truth, all despite an absence of biological imperative. We hold writers in such an incredibly high regard, and it's because we trust that they have something that can enhance our emotions, our thinking, our lives inside our lives. The voice they speak to the reader is partially that personal experience, everything from emotions and circumstances to accomplishments and failures. Most importantly, your experience is different from mine. And a beautiful thing happens when that voice turns into a successful reader experience. Though our lives are undeniably distinct, we find that we empathize with each other anyway. With some luck, honesty within yourself will transfer to the page.

That being said, that's only half the battle when developing a voice. Discovering one's own personal voice requires a lot of writing, too. A lot. A lot lot. And we may tend to forget that when we have a literary giant like George Saunders looming over us. He's so distinct that it's intimidating. It's important to remember that he's had an enormous amount of practice. He's not only published a bunch but he's kind of done it in our faces and with much success. That's rough when you're still in your voice-discovery phase. It's just important to appreciate how many long hours are behind *Civilwarland in Bad Decline,* for example. You have all the life/emotional experience in the world, but it's not going to matter much if you can't stitch it together with words on a page, or don't know how to develop character, how to use imagery.

JM: Craft knowledge and personal experience are both necessary to write remarkable fiction, sure. But if we believe in this concept of one writer having a consistent "voice," what does it mean for writers who experiment in many modes and voices? Is there still an argument to be made that even those who work in different forms, genres, mediums, etc. will still have some commonality that flags a "voice"? I think of the filmmaker Paul Thomas Anderson, who makes an entirely different type of film every time he write/directs, yet there is some shared DNA between all the films—a shared DNA that's sometimes hard to articulate in terms of specific decisions. Delillo strikes me, too; while his voice is often distinct, it's hard to find many voice-related commonalities between *Underworld* and *White Noise.* How does this idea of a writer having "one voice" hold up against versatility?

JH: I tend to think there's "shared DNA" in the most different of stories by the same author. That shared DNA may take the form of many subtle components, of which the author may or may not be consciously aware. Do they tend to favor one type of character over others? Maybe they use imagery a certain way. What about the way they note the passage of time? In your example, with Paul Thomas Anderson, despite his films being entirely different, maybe there is some similar tactic in his use of cinematography. In any case, you have to remember that the same mind is creating these two seemingly different pieces of art. Sure, experimentation with different forms and mediums happens, to the point where it might seem that a new voice is emerging, but I personally don't believe the apple falls far from the tree. Again, I'm a huge believer in personal experience shaping our character. No one shares your exact experiences.

In a sense then, I believe that voicefulness and versatility compete against one another. Finding a voice is a career-changing process which might limit the more exploratory or versatile attempt at a story. I know that some believe that we as writers have one good story within us, and we spend the rest of our time retelling it. It's a fun adage, and I can't remember from where it originates but, as a person who holds personal experience/emotions in such a high value, I regard that as mostly true. And from that arise all sorts of questions to ponder. Is versatility the absence of voice? Once established, are we imprisoned by our own voice, unable to shake free of our stories' implicit connectivity? It's a dark road to go down, at least for myself, because having a voice, on its own, initially seems more pro than con, doesn't it?

JM: If you'll allow me to go down this "dark road" a little more: it sounds to me that stating "all writers must have a distinctive voice" limits them from exploration—which you could consider "expanding" or "deepening" their voice. And that rewriting the same story over and over—if taken too firmly—will lead to a one-trick-pony scenario. Unless that phrase is meant very lightly—which I think it is—and means only that every writer inevitably covers similar thematic ground in each of their works because they're only telling another story from the same base worldview. Ultimately, it sounds preferential whether you make an active effort for all your stories to sound the same or whether you'll just write whatever appeals to you and assume there will be some commonality simply by virtue of the story coming from the same mind—and let the story itself dictate its own particular voice. I think the "voice" of a writer comes through unconsciously, rather than consciously. This goes back to what you were saying about authenticity, right? An authentic voice isn't so conscious of itself. So it makes sense to me that your transition—as you said—brought out your voice more. Please do correct me if I'm wrong in trying to articulate this, but transitioning gave your writing more confidence because you felt more authentic to yourself? Are you able to articulate—more specifically—what changed in your writing?

JH: I think that's a fair statement to make, as far as my transition bringing out my authentic voice. I mean, *you* try wearing a dress in public while still having beard shadow; it's a humbling experience, and it'll eventually make you confident in all aspects of your life, writing included. Myself personally, I was big into denial before transitioning. I had plenty of opportunities to come out to myself, though I refused to venture to that part of my own brain. But how can you be honest in your stories if you aren't honest within yourself? Honesty is the lifeblood of stories. Without it, the writer may jeopardize the empathy of which the reader is deserving.

I'd say the biggest change in my writing originates from the side of my consciousness I formerly kept so dim. There's more love now, definitely more love. I discovered that I had rivers of support from so many people, people who legitimately care for my happiness. As far as specificity goes, I know that the love I have for my sister, which was reinvigorated by her supporting my decision, is why "Trash Man" exists in the first place. My sister and I share a past, and for a long time she'd been the most consistent thing in my life, what with our parents splitting up, various changes in custody, unstable living arrangements. It was hard. And then we got older, and she moved away. It sucked for me, and we largely fell out of touch for a couple years. Somehow though, my sister ended up being the one who gave me my first makeover. Dressing like a girl was a Halloween "joke," but soon after I came out to her with the truth. You have to remember, that was during a time I was nervous about reactions and judgement the most. Coming out to her, that's what really brought us back to the same plane we were on as children, looking out for one another, being there emotionally for the other. Pure love. My sister is younger than me, but I've never imagined her as the little sister. She's so wise and true, and she understands people in ways that I still don't. And that's why the final confrontation scene operates the way it does in "Trash Man." Even though the brother is lost for answers on Corinne's departure, he knows that he loves her still. I'm not sure if that scene and these characters develop the way they do without me letting my sister back into my heart. I needed to have that experience for it to fully take form in my writing. And I'm super grateful to her for that, and I'm super grateful to myself to for that.

JM: Ahh—the honesty with yourself *directly* shaped this story—not only in terms of themes or voice. I hadn't realized the story was so firmly rooted in autobio—the divorcing parents, the sister relationship, etc. Could we delve into the other elements, then? Where does the titular character originate from? The trash piling up? The carousel? The image of the character lying on a bloody mattress? Rory? Obviously, many of these elements are fictitious, but now that you've talked about how heavily inspired the story is from your own life, I'd be curious to hear what other elements are repurposed. Is this amount of autobiography typical? What role does autobiography play in your fiction?

JH: First off, I think at least a modicum of autobiography makes it into all my stories. This is not, for example, the first time I've written about a missing sister. And sometimes the autobiographical element isn't content-based at all. Frequently, it's an observation or a question, and it just snowballs from there. A friend might tell me a funny and embarrassing story and my reaction is to wonder if this happened to a different, less stable person. What would that story look like? Having set that as a foundation, however, I also have two major influences concerning autobiographical elements to my stories: Agatha Christie and George Saunders. To expound on the former, I was, and still am, a monster Agatha Christie fan. In the preface to *The Body in the Library*, she confesses an inspiration to write the novel because of a certain conspicuous family she sees in a hotel. She then explains, "Fortunately they left the next day, so that my imagination could get to work unhampered by any kind of knowledge." I mean, this represents to me just how badass this lady was and is. It takes an incredible amount of respect and humility to generate stories this way—respect and humility in the sense of admitting the author is never bigger than the story, that the story should be able to take on a life of its own. In the end, that's all we have as readers, isn't it? Just the pure story, no author hanging over our shoulder enumerating on what symbolizes what, how this paragraph should be read, telling us what we should be feeling. Even though I had a general content-based idea for "Trash Man"—a brother and sister who drift apart and then come back together—I didn't know how events, interactions, and scenes would pan out. I was in the same boat as, hopefully, the reader, as far as not quite knowing what was going to happen next but excited to find out. I think that storytelling calls for a certain degree of listening as well. And that's really what is at the core of good writing. Allowing the story to become autonomous at times.

JM: The story is cohesive despite the seat-of-your-pants writing style; it seems that method really worked out for this story—and its unexpected developments in particular.

JH: I like to think so. As for Saunders influencing my philosophy of autobiography in fiction, that started in classroom some years ago. My writing professor, Bruce Machart, gave me an issue of *Glimmer Train*, telling me it was the first magazine in which he'd been published. Saunders was featured in the magazine in the form of an interview and that was actually the first time I read him. The interview became more relevant when I came back to it a second time and had by then read many of his collections. Beyond that distinct voice you mentioned earlier, Saunders' stories are noteworthy in the sense of how fantastical and surreal they are. On that, Saunders says, "My idea is that life is so strange and so unknowable and so beautiful that you might have to resort to extraordinary means to really get some of that on the page." I think what he's trying to say is that something is lost in translation when we take a real, vivid experience and try to write about it; words can only do so much. And the way to deal with that is to overcompensate, exaggerate, dramatize. Hence, that is why we get these outlandish, quirky stories from him.

Right so, what's the deal, how does that apply to Trash Man? What is autobiographical and what's not? I'm sitting here and I want so bad to tell you that everything from the carousel to the bloody mattress is somehow rooted in nonfiction, just to make my life sound a bit more interesting (though, I'm glad to say my sister never laid tacks in my shoes or *anything* remotely like that). Honestly not much is autobiographical outside of what I've already mentioned. The parents splitting up, as well as the arc of the brother and sister's relationship, is rooted in truth, yes. And sure, I lived in a neighborhood that had a pond with sun fish in it, and I used to see kids flying kites down there, but Trash Man, the junk, Rory, the carousel, Mrs. Leeks with her megaphone, they're all complete imagination. What's certainly not imaginary is the feeling injected into that surrealist background. I love my sister despite all the junk and trash in between childhood and the present; under that is love, good times, and memories worth having. That's the *feeling* I wished to enhance.

JM: I've noticed a lot of the writers we've published over the past two years have readily admitted to Saunders being one of their biggest influences. Our other story this issue arguably has a dash of Saunders, too. What do you think it is about oddity, absurdism, and surrealism that's making it catch on—particularly now? We've got a reality tv show host as president and corporatism is at an all-time high; the idea of helping strangers with your tax money—democratic socialism—is laughed at by a sizeable amount of the population; white nationalism and bigotry is on the rise only fifty or sixty years after it was supposedly suppressed in a world war that millions died from. All of this to say that the old phrase of truth being stranger than fiction seems true day-by-day. Do you think the contemporary lean towards absurdism has something to do with current events?

JH: Totally, I've noticed an uptick in absurdism as well. At least in the workshops I've been in, absurdism and surrealism, too, is in good supply. I might call it a resurgence though; we can't forget the impact of the Kafkas and Samuel Becketts left unto western civilization. Perhaps they and writers in that category are getting a second, third, and forth glance. After all, the mid-twentieth century wasn't all that long ago. Still, something else seems to be at work here. The events you've listed certainly share the responsibility as far as influencing non-traditional fiction. The world is undeniably strange, to the point where putting it on paper as fiction can raise plausibility issues with your writing professor. More significant than that, however, is the accessibility to that strange information. That's something that is different about the twentieth century and beyond. We hear about these just ludicrous happenings, constantly. Think about OJ Simpson, Michael Jackson, the Tide Pods incidents, and, yes, the celebrity status of our current president. Word travels fast these days, with social media, television, and radio as primary news sources. Absurdist stories tap into what I believe to be a symptom of American (maybe even global) anxiety. We now have to contend with the strangeness of not only our neighbors but those outside our immediate circles. That's a lot of people, a lot of strangeness. Absurdism might just be the expression of that.

JM: Following up that grand question, let's jump into a few more specific, craft-focused questions now; there's plenty of great craft on display in "Trash Man," all worth talking through. One interesting decision I noticed was the constant fluctuation between reported dialogue and direct dialogue. Sometimes even within the same conversation you'll switch back and forth between the two. Could you try to articulate your decision-making process there? How do you know what should be reported and what should be directly given?

JH: Dialogue when it's coming from a character's mouth is probably among the most fun parts of a story to write. But dialogue is versatile, as you've pointed out, and there's much to be implied when we use it directly or whether it's alive outside quotation marks. Enjoyable as it is to write, I find that when it comes to direct dialogue, less is more. For example, Trash Man's speech on Little Summer Ave is reported, sandwiched between two bits of direct dialogue, "Fuck yeah" and "Your Dad's good." The spoken dialogue is succinct, showing he commands at least some degree of respect in the former statement. In the latter, we have the embodiment of the entire neighborhood's opinion in Corinne's claim: he's saving them all from themselves and that deserves their appreciation. Those two bits of dialogue are intended to do a lot of work in only a handful of words, a point I'll return to shortly. The reason why Trash Man's speech is left out is because we may infer it. The reader can basically guess what Trash Man says because we know that he takes on everybody's trash. The narrator has been telling us that from the outset of the story. There's no need to belabor the point or slow the pace down to record what the reader already knows. Time is so very important in this piece. Even though it's a relatively short story, it characterizes a period of several years. As such, even the direct dialogue often ends up being short-winded. If long exchanges were too frequent in this story, it would ground the reader in a certain time period and then it would be disruptive to shake them out of it. That's namely the reason why Trash Man offering Dad a beer, Dad telling the kids to come to the table, and the like, are reported. Do we, as the reader, really need to know the finer points of the George fire that Mom probably tells to the kids? Of course not. We know the kids probably did hear them, as that is what's plausible, but I don't think it's necessary to the understanding of the story as a whole. Rather, I prefer to reserve the impactful stuff for the quotes. That way, by the virtue of what is being prioritized, the reader knows that, hey, this next quote is probably going to be important in terms of character development or plot. That's why, *hopefully*, the argument scenes have the power they have; why Corinne's comment, about Mom being a thousand miles away and herself down the street, hurts and heals so much.

JM: All that sounds right to me; reporting dialogue is very useful for pacing, for resisting repetition, for unimportant dialogue—all of which you've said in some form above. And if you've established a consistent use of reported dialogue, it puts extra stress on the direct dialogue—flagging it as important. The direct dialogue suddenly hits harder. This also seems to me to be a good way to bring the themes more subtly to the forefront: you can put stresses on dialogue that can hold double meanings. But let's stay on the topic of how important *time* is in this piece. Often times, when a short story tries to cram multiple years into a short word count, it feels rushed—mental whiplash. Or the writing gives in to excessive narration, summary, and skimming. "Trash Man" is still quickly paced, of course, but that's different from a story feeling *rushed*. Outside of utilizing reported dialogue, what other craft techniques did you use to keep the story well-paced despite covering so much time?

JH: Well, it was a huge effort to avoid that "rushed" feeling. It's so easy to get excited about a story, excited about change and development, that we may forget to ease up and take our time. Even in a story of this length there is room to do that—but just how I endeavored to accomplish that, I'll get to in a moment. First, I have to acknowledge the more minor—but still important—technique of using certain indicator phrases. For example, the story will often continue thusly: "By this time..." "Most nights..." "In a year,

Corinne would go to the mailbox..." These phrases keep the reader at least vaguely aware that time is passing as we march on. It is such that the effect is not jarring as we read that the narrator now has a job, facial hair, has graduated. I didn't want the reader to ever ask, "Wait, when did he get old enough to get a job—I thought he was just playing on the carousel?" I mentioned that there was enough time here to slow the story down, to let the story breathe. Honestly, the other major influence on this story besides my sister, was a story by Saunders called "Isabelle." I was in shock at how Saunders was able to characterize a young man's entire life through the course of a mere seven or so pages; I'd never successfully emulated that before, at least not to my own satisfaction. So, I spent a lot of time with "Isabelle," marking up indicator phrases not unlike my own, and noting when and how time was passing. It didn't feel rushed in the slightest. And so, Trash Man was born in part for the love I have for my sister as I said, and part for experimentation. What I discovered in Saunders' story was that if you pair concrete images, which also reflect a passing of time, it'll make the marching pace appear more seamless. For instance, you'll notice the sentences, "The mounds in Trash Man's yard toppled from sheer height. Our grass grew green." The reader may infer that time is passing because the mounds of trash are starting to topple. Additionally, the reader knows that time is passing to the point where the residents' grass, ostensibly covered with trash, is able to grow green again. It ended up going a long way, thankfully, and I appreciate that Saunders helped me discover that.

JM: An extremely close reading of an author you admire; great advice for our readers (most of whom are writers). I quite like the concrete indicators of time passing. Of course, we all know the "show; don't tell" rule. What you've described is a great method of *showing* the passing of time, rather than simply telling us through the indicator phrases you mentioned. Of course, there will be occasional moments when the phrase indicators are necessary to keep the narrative timeline clear, but the story leaning into the concrete *showing* of time passing is surely a stronger move.

This is also a very concisely written story, which I

think helps with the pacing. Each line is packed to the brim with great detail work, and no line is wasted in moving the plot forward—the story never idles in the way that so much unpublished fiction does. Could you talk a little more about the pacing on a sentence-level—not just in terms of time passing, but in terms of the story's heavy detail work and momentum?

JH: You've got the right of it. Every line should be focused on either moving the plot forward or on development—of character, story arc, etc—which is arguably the same thing. Literally aim that high to the point of ridiculousness. Take for instance, that the boxes Dad drops off one day are "flattened-out boxes." When you want to be descriptive, you need to be specific; it makes the scene more vivid. That part we know right off the bat. That's half the reason the boxes are flattened-out. The other half is because they signify to the reader that Dad has made an effort to be courteous to Trash Man, presumably the way the whole neighborhood would be expected to be after such a deep sacrifice. Compare this to the moment later on, when Dad momentarily loses his appreciation for Trash Man, grousing about how he should start a pick-up service. By that point, people are quite literally dumping their garbage in his driveway, without the courtesy of stepping out of their car. It's that insensitivity that later gives Trash Man spinal issues as he attempts to reorganize all the garbage. It looks like a minor choice to just be specific and thus more vivid, but the dual- and multiple-purposed descriptions are crucial to time efficiency when telling a story. You never want to waste your reader's time; it's precious and deserves to be respected.

Next, if you mention something more than once in your writing, you want to make a mental note and attach significance to that item. No idle items, make sure they have a purpose. I think of the carousel, probably the most important object to the story. It's doing a lot of work just by virtue of existing. First, it foreshadows the trash accumulating, that's the easy bit. Tied to that purpose, it also characterizes Trash Man as the type of person who would keep trash in his lawn. The carousel is broken "garbage," but he's essentially keeping it there for the kids to play on. This makes it plausible for his character to do something like allow people to use his property as a dump. Most importantly, the carousel comes to symbolize an innocent, playful, and loving childhood. Despite its nature of being basically repurposed trash, it is nonetheless a memory made positive by two siblings. That's why the story ends the way it does, cyclically returning to the carousel. These two siblings are returning to a time full of love and care for each other. They, but namely the narrator, need only to look beneath the garbage to find that carousel.

JM: Ending on an image, too, is always a sharp move. The story doesn't only cover a good chunk of time; it also covers quite a lot of narrative. As short as the story is, we've got three plots (and several relationships) moving at once: (1) the trash man backdrop narrative; (2) the protagonist's coming of age (his relationships with his sister and parents); (3) Rory's struggle for self-worth (his relationships with Corrine and his father). Talk to us about the difficulties of juggling all three in such a short space.

JH: Stories are never really "about" what is said in their summaries, or perhaps what'd you'd read in their book jacket. Stories are stories within stories. I think about how even the stories we see in the nascence of our reading career are crafted less around these two talking fish having an argument or what have you, and more around a revelation of moral character, how we should treat others, and so on. It's my hope that the reader finds it reductive to say that "Trash Man" is about this dude who lets everyone throw trash in his yard. To me that sounds wrong. And the three subplots that you've observed seem to be the best way to describe the story as a whole. Was that hard for me to write? Absolutely. Making all three of those things tie together, *while* also keeping pace, *while* also trying to be entertaining for the reader—it was a formidable task. But the key is in listening to the story as it goes, and I mean that as metaphysically as possible. I largely don't consider this a story of my own. Once it's on the page, I lose ownership of it because it belongs to itself and has its own identity. I could not tell you for sure that Corinne and Rory get married, as likely as that seems. That's outside the boundaries of the story and I have no business dictating that. I'm not convinced that young writers hear that side enough, that the story has its own will to exist and you can either choose to listen to it or choose to manipulate it. Sometimes it comes out good either way, for a skilled writer, just not for me. My entire process, even laying down those three subplots, is given over to the story's will. I have *opinions* of those plots. For example, I think that it was fair to Rory to have a moment within all these other important relationships—mom vs dad and sister vs brother—where the reader is reminded he's gosh darn human being, and he does deserve things like love and care; I think that the subplots talk to each other, that they're all relevant and deserving of the stage time they have been given. Having said that, I can't lay too much claim to "owning" the story, more that I have allowed it into being what it is.

JM: I think balancing these three plots goes back to our talk about pacing; you keep the reader interested due to the plot's purposefully speedy momentum. There's always something happening; when you're done with one plot for the time being, you quickly move to the next. There are three ongoing plots to fill the space, after all.

The story has a nice tightness to it that I suspect demanded cutting during revision. In fact, I remember you cut a small scene during revisions with *Driftwood*. I hadn't recommended it, but I think it was a smart cut. Could you share that scene with the readers and talk about why you cut it? Were there other scenes that suffered cuts in your tightening of the writing?

JH: Haha, okay, right. Mr. Freddy Klip and his drawings. Originally what I had was:

"The guilty couldn't throw anything away without risking it to be seen by anyone braving the streets. The worst we'd seen was Freddy Klips' nude pencil drawings of women in the neighborhood. In the pictures, the women were being branded and flogged and crammed into limb-binding positions. A tree branch had impaled a wind-blown drawing. 'I gave it up,' he said when Katrina Hartman confronted him. 'That's why it's in the trash, I gave it up!' It was such that the

picture—of Katrina Hartman squatting over a bundle of log-sized Chiquita bananas, idiotically signed Freddy K. in the corner—was posted in a format somewhat like a community message board. We'd all seen it and it must have been a lot like Martin's 95 Theses but with sadism. But the branch was too high for Katrina to reach, so she had a telephone tech reach it with his cherry picker. He asked if he could keep the drawing as a reward. When Katrina said hell no he waited for her to turn around and tucked it into his waistband."

First of all, it always bothered me that Freddy Klip got a last name for no other reason than so we can laugh that he signed it on the drawings. Getting his full name also gives the impression that he's an important character. Really, he never shows up again. Nor does Katrina Hartman. We don't even get the last name of the narrator's family, and yet, what makes this perv and this woman so special? Not much. At least in my opinion.

And going back to what you asked me about detail work, I didn't want to waste the reader's time. There was just no versatility in Freddy's scene. It's a good laugh, sure, but it detracted from the actual plot. Along the same principle, I did end up cutting other moments like that too, at the recommendation of the *Driftwood* team—edits that I genuinely agree needed to be made. In the same vein as the Freddy scene, there was another where a very sexually frustrated hipster throws a rock through someone's car window because he believed his girlfriend wouldn't fellate him due to the garbage in his lawn (you know, typical reasons to damage another person's property). There were also dogs shitting in houses instead of the streets, a penis on one of the carousel horses, and "decapitated" dolls, all of which were just too distracting to the story. The danger there is that such descriptions will rip the reader out of the story, forcing them to notice that they are indeed *reading* and not experiencing.

That's the thing about editors. You hear a whole lot about the reader and writer relationship, but rarely about how the editor(s) fit in. It's so easy to get tunnel vision when you're writing a story. As you write it, you live in it. To a fault, I sometimes begin to accept things as plausible just because I have spent so much time with it. That's why a skilled editor is so essential to the writing process. They read to read, and often see past the story the writer can sometimes be blind to.

JM: Those last few cuts you mentioned had to do with our on-going conversation about quirk, and how a story could overrely on it, risking sensationalism and distracting from an otherwise powerful narrative. Talk to me about how you perceive "quirk" in stories. When is it good to grab the reader's attention? How do you determine what is going too far?

JH: I understand quirk to be an odd or strange quality to a story that somehow slightly brings us out of the realm of realism. Like anything else, a quirk should implicitly or explicitly add to the story, give it meaning. Usually you can get this for free as long as the writer teaches the reader early on that this a stranger world. That's why the first paragraph of "Trash Man" is so very important, why it's the first thing the reader has to get through. I want them to think, "Okay, this is not going to be a normal story if garbage trucks are not a thing for this neighborhood." By being upfront with that fact, it limits the need to be realistically plausible later on. I do not want the reader to be surprised that garbage trucks aren't coming halfway through the story: "Well, Jessica, I don't think that this would happen in real life. I mean, why would the trucks just not come? Why wouldn't someone call the Department of Waste Management and complain?" If I'm inviting those questions, I've done something wrong. Be upfront with your quirks, don't save them as surprises for your readers to dissect later.

That being said, you don't want to drop too many quirk bombs. That can sometimes steal the spotlight from the main source of conflict, which is why you all at *Driftwood* recommended certain cuts in the first place. More than confusing the spotlight, that added quirkiness can, as you've phrased, *grab* attention. I try to steer clear of grabbing attention when I write and instead try to *keep* attention. If you grab attention there is potential to interrupt the fictive dream, a term used by John Gardner in *The Art of Fiction* to describe the trance-like state we experience when we read a story. That's a precious thing the writer is constantly try to keep intact throughout the whole narrative.

JM: Highlighting the unreality early is extremely important, and I like your distinction between keeping and grabbing attention. What's the relationship of quirk to absurdism or surrealism?

JH: Same genus, different species. Both quirk and surrealism/absurdism are activated by an implausible scenario. The wolf has a job at an insurance company; the mirrors only reflect images of Queen Elizabeth; a giant ceiling is descending upon us to crush us into the earth. Quirk though, I would say, is a tool for surrealism/absurdism to utilize. I'm not sure "Trash Man" would end with the same credibility it has if I did not stick certain lines in reader's face throughout. The quirky description of the megaphone lady, the fact that trash literally towers over Rory's house, the bloody mattress scene—those are all helping to do the work of keeping the story surreal and absurd, which allows for the almost ghost-like ending that we get. Kid versions of themselves running around and feeling emotions and stuff? What's the deal with that? If this were pure realism, that scene doesn't go over well. At the same time, you have to remember not to overwhelm the reader with those quirks, like we mentioned earlier. Quirks are, in a lot of ways, meant to clarify the surrealism/absurdism.

JM: We're in danger here of using surrealism and absurdism interchangeably—and we shouldn't since they're entirely separate genres. Both deal with "unreality," but one of their key differences (among many) is that surrealism is often unreality played for drama, whereas absurdism is often unreality played for comedy/satire. Which camp does "Trash Man" fall into, if either?

JH: I would add that they both deal with rational thought as well. An important aspect of absurdism is that we as humans seek rational thought out in the world and ultimately don't find any. I think of *Waiting For Godot*. Whereas, surrealism openly subverts rational in order to achieve a higher level of unconscious thought and thus a truer freedom of expression (Hello, Kafka). That, coupled with your assertion that surrealism is unreality played for drama and tension, indicates to me that "Trash Man" is more a surrealist piece of fiction than absurdist. It is, after all, a story that prioritizes a feeling over everything else. It's that quirky component of the story—trash piling up—that enhances the brother-sister arc. And while the story is funny (hopefully), I tend not to think it's satirical, nor do I think rationality is on the chopping block the way it is in other absurdist pieces.

JM: I'd say your story has a dash of each, but it's probably best categorized a little more broadly as magical realism. Categorizing is a bit reductive anyways, so it's probably best to say the story has a dash of [blank] than to stick it entirely in one category.

You mentioned Saunders and Christie earlier, but what other writers have had a significant impact on "Trash Man" and your writing more broadly? And how about other mediums, such as film, art, music, etc?

JH: Sometimes Trash Man will dip into this communal "we," and that's definitely a result of how many times I've read *The Virgin Suicides* by Jeffrey Eugenides. I've pleaded with friends to read that book, forced them to watch the film adaptation (not as wonderful, admittedly), and written blog posts on it. It's just a dark and hilarious book with a narration style that has always grabbed me and took me to the moon. I've tried to emulate it in other stories, in the way of experimentation not unlike I've done with Saunders' "Isabelle." There's just something about that we're-all-in-this-together style that ramps up the tension and makes conflict just delicious; because if there's a "we," then there's often a "they" who "we" are competing against, someone outside the circle. And it's just fun to watch those two components clash.

Another author who has impacted my writing is Miranda July. I first read her short story collection *No one belongs here more than you* at the behest of an old college friend. Those stories operate in this odd liminal space between realism and full-on quirk. They're intense, emotionally driven stories that read like poetry at times. And God, that woman knows how to be funny. I've always appreciated that, as you can already tell by my preference in writers. To be hilarious within a

story that initially sounds like it has no business being funny—that's special. To be honest, I've been working on a novel in my very limited free time with Miranda July in mind the most. She does such a good job with her quirkiness, and her methods never feel misplaced. That's something I totally have a lot of respect for.

If I try to involve another art form in my writing, it's probably music. When I sympathize with an emotion, I will try to invoke it in my writing—but *just* the feeling, nothing to do with content or verbatim lyrics. I keep returning to "Let Me Go" (Hailee Steinfeld & Alesso) for the compassion. And "Take Me Home" (Cash Cash) for the duality—energy conflated with heartbreak. It's strange the connections we make when we experience somebody else's art. And it's kind of magical to see one form influence another. That being said, I'm compiling a playlist of EDM tracks, with no to limited lyrics, and cranking the volume while I write. I've heard of classical music being able to help corral some writing, so I'd like it a try with my favorite genre, which inherently doesn't have much in the way of lyrics to distract my own wording.

JM: Tell me more about your novel.

JH: It's still in its early stages. There's a laundry list of literature I have to read before and during the writing process. I can't write if I'm not reading at the same time. My subconscious likes to play in the world of whatever book I'm currently reading; it bleeds into my writing that way. A lot of times it's in a good way—it helps me decide my own pathways. What's working in this book that I like? What isn't working? It's for that reason that I'm going to choose very deliberately which texts I read while I write.

I'm still getting to know characters, still meeting some others. I did find my protagonist and I've spent some time with her outsides the margins of the story. She'll be my first attempt at a fully realized transgender character, which I'm excited about. I don't want to mention too, too much because I find that I write stories better when no one knows much about them. It's weird, that's how I've killed stories in the past. I talk about them before they're finished and it kind of eliminates the need for me to tell it in ink. I will say that it'll be a novel in surrealism, and that the protagonist—Fink is her name—meets a wide variety of quirky people with colorful jobs. My favorite job is Fink's though, because she works in a place called Madame Rover's Crying Cafe, which is exactly what it sounds like. A place where people with fragile egos go in order to feel better about themselves. And how is that? By yelling at and harassing servers to the point that they cry. Because sometimes, you have to lash out at strangers in order to feel better about the poor, sad life you're living. No gratuity? No problem! Tips are always optional! See? Exactly what you expected.

JM: Sounds like that'll be plenty of fun to write—and plenty of difficult to write well. Keep me in the loop and let me know how it goes. Why do you think telling people about your works-in-progress kill the magic for you?

JH: A couple things. Unless they're offering some kind of constructive criticism, it takes away from the reader's experience entirely. And the reader's experience should always be of vital importance to the writer. Stories are rarely about the author's intentions. They're more about execution of those intentions. As such, the story must have the will to exist on its own two feet, without further aid of the author. No summaries, no expositions, no disclaimers. Once the writer begins their story, they enter a tacit agreement that they are not present for the consumption of that story. I understand that this may be a radical opinion. After all, understanding a greater context outside the story or novel can help add clarity to its greater meaning. That *is* what happens in academia, surely, every time a book is taught. Be that as it may, I still think that the story itself boasts more power than the writer who penned it. That's why the magic dies a little for me when I "tell" it to prospective readers.

As for the next reason: well, sometimes I *can't* talk about it at all. Simply because I don't know enough about it. I used to plot out stories meticulously. Scene by scene, symbol by symbol. You know what that was? Boring. More boring than an aquarium sans fish. I find it exciting, as the writer, to not exactly know what is coming next; potential is just boundless. I find that the stories I write now, without the planning, are better than the ones I used to. "Trash Man" is one such story created in that way. I may have had an *idea* towards the arc of the siblings' relationship, but I didn't know how I was going to fulfill that on page one, or on page four for that matter. There are a thousand details in that story that I did not preconceive. That's how the best ones are crafted though, at least for me. It feels less like I'm trying to force something and more like I'm allowing a story into existence.

JM: Well, let's not risk killing the magic anymore. Thanks for working through this interview—and all the critiques—with me, Jessica. Are there any parting words you have for our readers?

JH: My pleasure. I know you and your team work hard to bring this magazine to all your readers. You do a fantastic job every issue. I wish you continued success, and keep reading, all.

THE
TAXIDERMIST

SETH BRADY TUCKER

The smell of lilac detergent and old blood and something long dead met him at the top of the stairs, the lone bulb stabbed into the jaundiced wall lonely and dark when he flipped the switch. Parsons pulled a tiny LED flashlight from his belt and began the slow walk down. The air held the odd warmth that occupies cold spaces, musty and fetid and damp and full of living things breathing tiny microscopic breaths. Parsons had been called there to find an animal, which meant it would likely be to clean up a mess. He settled down on the last wooden step, lit a cigarette, scanned the corners, assumed he would find whatever it was he was meant to discover back behind the old boiler ticking in the corner.

Parsons had a black garbage bag for vermin and he had a blue bag for beloved pets, bags which he used to carry the dead to his shop to be recreated with the help of glues and straw and molds.

He finished his cigarette and ground it out, kicked it down the mouth of a damp drain. On the few sagging shelves were an assortment of old bicycle tires and boxes of shiny fabrics and frilly coils of ribbon and amateurish carved wooden toys. He rose to his feet, found nothing behind the boiler, and only after exhausting all other locations did he think to follow the smell, and there it was: an orange and dusty dead cat pressed up behind some boxes as if it was hiding from something. He couldn't decide which bag applied to the situation, so he began to stuff the stiff carcass of the tabby into the blue one. Upstairs, he heard a door open and close, a voice singing out high-pitched and wan.

He wondered if maybe he'd entered the wrong house; he had assumed it was abandoned when he found the front door ajar and hasp broken, the general lack of furniture making the house feel bigger than it was and twice as empty. He was tempted for a moment to dump the dried body of the cat back behind the shelves. Again, a woman's voice from above, then hard sharp steps that sounded like a hammer on marble. The footsteps drew nearer so he called out, just loud enough to be heard, "Hello, this is Jack? From *Every Living Thing Taxidermy*? Someone called us?"

It was quiet. The boiler made a hissing sound then burped and he could smell oil. The rap on the floor above resumed and the door at the top of the stairs opened and even though the light from behind the figure distorted everything, it was clearly the slender figure of a young boy or girl. A boy, he decided, from the long arms and big head. A child, of all things, he thought, alone with him here in an abandoned house.

Parsons Taxidermy and Animal Control was situated in the middle of a stark old shopping center for decades, what was the post office on one side then later a bookstore separated by just a single concrete wall. On the other side a café, then a gun shop, then a Jazzercise studio, then the 80's came and went and Reagan and LA Gear and leg-warmers went out of fashion and it was vacant for a time until a local lady from the LDS church scrubbed the space and converted it into a dance studio. No one knew what his father was into before they found the cameras, what he actually did to those kids, whether some awful physical threshold had been breached—but it was clear from what they found in his storage locker that he was filming them all through the walls from a bunch of angles, starting with dance floor to locker room to bathrooms—and though no one came forward to say what kind of monster he was exactly, it didn't take Jeremiah Parsons long to figure nothing good was coming of a visit to the shops by the Sheriff and a band of deputies. Jeremiah Parsons must have been watching the scene through his cameras, because when the deputies finished examining his work in the studio, he was already climbing up into the rafters and squirming over between the old dropped ceiling and the roof, kicking in the asbestos paneling so that he could hop down and into that dance studio. He shot himself in front of his own cameras with a thirty-aught-six; the sheriff and deputy could hear it play through the computer speakers in the office and the sharp report of the rifle echoed next door. They found him perched on the barrel of the weapon as if he were trying to swallow it, his lips dripping an opaque blood down the wooden stock and steel handgrip.

The little boy at the top of the stair was not going away. He put his hand petulantly on his hip, demanded, "Who are you down there?"

"Jack," he said, "from *Every Living Thing Taxidermy.*"

"I di'nt call for no ride."

Parsons thought about correcting him, then didn't. What kind of conversation would that be anyway? The boy was lean, had on a lavender top and white jeans so tight and bleached that they looked pink. About nine years old, he guessed. The kid stepped out of the light and Parsons realized what it was making the sound: sequined purple tap shoes. On hardwood. His father had called them sea-queens, he remembered, laughing at his own joke as he stretched hide over a deer mold. The boy disappeared and he heard the hard-tapping move across what he imagined was the living room, then softer taps on the kitchen linoleum. He didn't want to go up the stairs, have a talk alone with a kid, so he sat on the bottom stair and lit another cigarette, tied off the top of the bag and set it at his feet. He hoped the boy would simply leave.

Outside, the sun came out from gray clouds and pitched a line of light down into the basement, and he could see that the concrete walls were painted in swirls and flowers, invisible in the dark behind the shelves, and before the sun went back behind those clouds he could see the shine of brass along the walls in every direction, then a face peeking out from behind them too, and Parsons let out a yelp of surprise until he realized that one wall was covered in mirrors and what he was seeing was his own face, lean and lined and only vaguely recognizable: familiar and obscene. He ran his hand along the old brass bar, imagined what it would have looked like to see a dancer arching her back, foot up on the bar. He pinched the cigarette dead, watching his reflection, and it was like seeing his father. The sound of shuffling and tapping on carpet then linoleum again, like a trout flapping from mud to gravel. He gathered the cat and flashlight and prepared to head up. He stopped to touch his reflection, gave it a soft punch with his knuckles. It was the similarities around the mouth, he thought, that made people recoil from him.

A dancing studio. It seemed impossible to Parsons, like some colossally unfunny joke. It occurred to him that the call might have been fake, that this was just some prank, or worse, that he was being set up for a very unfunny and cruel punishment by some local who still needed to see someone pay for what his father had done. He picked up the blue bag and carried it up the stairs.

The boy sat at a bar counter in the old kitchen, eating cereal out of an old plastic margarine container. The kitchen was bare, cupboards open and empty, the air cool and unmoving, just the buzz of the old refrigerator, which clunked to a stop as he spoke. "Do you live here?" he asked.

The boy slurped up another mouthful, shrugged his thin shoulders, then mumbled, "Ya shun't smoke in here."

The room was chilly, but the boy didn't seem to notice. Parsons asked again and the boy clacked his shoes on his chair, let his arm flow out as if he were practicing a ballet move, slowly brought his hand to his lips, kissed his fingers and then flashed jazz hands and sparkled fingertips. "Sometimes," then, "depends."

On *what*, Parsons thought but didn't ask. "Well, I have this cat," he said, trailing off, holding the bag up. "I was asked by someone to check here for their cat. They told me this home was unoccupied, but that they hadn't seen it around, so I came down to check."

The boy didn't answer, just got up and began to tap, then tapped his way over to the fridge where he set the milk all alone on a shelf, just a couple empty bottles of beer and what looked like takeout ketchup and mustard packs flattened at the bottom. The smell of moldy bread, the semi-sweet scent of rotten apples. "This is mine," he said, moving his milk back further.

"Is that where you practice? In the dance studio downstairs?" Parsons asked the boy, trying finally to get something, anything from the kid. He snapped his flashlight on his belt next to his dart gun, adjusted his pants, dropped the bag to the floor, and leaned back on the counter facing the boy. The window over the sink faced a rotting crabapple tree, bent as if it were trying to peer into the house.

"That was the ol' lady's thing," the boy said. "Down there, she had a record player and thought all us kids was gonna be happy to practice." The boy gave a tap flourish, left his arms outspread, hands peaked like the neck of a swan. "Know what? With her gone I can dance anywhere though," he finished, one big final flurry of arm swinging and taps, then sat again to continue eating.

"Who was this old lady?" Parsons asked. He felt suddenly that everything would make sense if he could just figure out who had called him. "Does this old lady live here?"

"Nope. She was just an ol' lady. Silver hair and weird dresses. But she give us lessons free." The boy finished the last bite, fishing and fishing until he had the 'O' trapped in the spoon, slowly slurped it down, made eye contact, appraising him, seemed to come to some sort of conclusion: "She let me stay here sometime."

"Well, I have the cat. The old tabby?" Parsons reached down, held up the bag again, set it down.

The boy started laughing. "The old *Tabby*? You mean *Biscuits*?" he cried, like he couldn't believe it. "Shoot, that wa'nt no one's pet. Mean as road tar. No other cats left around here but that'un." He jumped to his feet and started doing soft-shoe taps, shuffling this way and that. "Biscuits was the last one to survive the foxes they put in the park to kill the rats." He flourished then. "See? Watch this," and the boy went into a frenzied and mad dance. "I can practice my dances anywhere," he finished, and an imagined top-hat rolled down his arm to his open hand. His fingernails, Parsons noticed, were painted with bright blue glitter and his skin was so white it was translucent and marbled with veins.

They looked at each other, and the boy smiled and licked the milk from his lips like a kitten. It occurred to Parsons that the boy might be living in the house, and he wondered how to ask that question without taking on the responsibility for the child, without acknowledging this boy could be his responsibility.

When the doorbell rang, they both started. Parsons bounced off the counter, the boy skipped clack-ety-clack before he started to run silently on his heels and around the corner of the kitchen, then down the stairs into the basement. He stopped at the door and turned and put his finger to his lips, shushing Parsons before closing the door.

Parsons didn't know what to do—he tried the back door but it was bolted with the key-hole on the inside—so he grabbed the bag and his gear and presented himself at the door, ready to answer any questions that were sure to come his way. Doing his work is all, he would tell them. He got a call to find a cat, he would say. Outside, a woman in a muumuu stood with one arm under a breast, the other set upon it to help her smoke her cigarette, her hand held over her mouth against the cold.

"Who's you?" she said as he opened the door, all the authority in the world residing in those who have nothing to do. She looked beyond him into the interior, "Whut ya doing in Miss Lorna house?"

"Jack Parsons, *All Living Things Taxidermy*?" He hated that he said his name like a question. "I was sent here by a family looking for their cat?" There it was again, that lilt to his speech. He felt the cold tickling his nerves, his fellow townsfolk now people to be feared.

The woman had gray hair trickling from under a leather cap, and her skin seemed blue from the breeze, ashy and lacking color. She looked up and down the street as if expecting someone as she finished her cigarette and tucked the butt into her front pocket. When she moved her hand he could see why she hid behind folded arms: her throat was swollen and lopsided with a goiter, a visible mole pushed out like a nipple and covered in long black hairs. She appraised him before she spoke, "I know that name. You the son of Jeremiah Parsons? Over Riverton way? The pedophile?"

It was like his father's breath fluttered icy on the hair of Parsons neck. He stepped to the side, tried to maneuver onto the concrete patio in order to close the door behind him so he could simply walk away. The woman blocked his way when she saw the boy emerge from the basement with a flourish, when he said sullenly, like it was routine, "Howdy, Miss Gunther." The woman's eyes tracked Parsons as the boy came up to stand behind him, a knowing frown on her face, her dull eyes suddenly alive.

"That was my pop," Parsons explained, "but everyone knows I had nothing to do with that business."

Over the course of the weeks following his father's suicide, Parsons was followed by deputies and police officers, pulled over and searched, one night even manhandled into a cruiser and then to the Sherriff's office to see how he would react to the video footage of the kids, all of them in different levels of undress, until finally the Sherriff himself lost his temper and showed Parsons his father's suicide 'by accident.' He was visibly disappointed when Parsons didn't flinch as his father pulled the trigger. Parsons didn't understand why the man had such a hard-on for him until he did: a daughter, blonde and thin in photos all through his office. Photos of the Sherriff and his wife and daughter filled one wall, the girl growing older but the wife disappearing from them, the daughter knobby and frail, then the most recent was of her dancing across a stage. The Sherriff saw where his gaze fell, stepped in front of Parsons before ushering him back into the interrogation room.

Finally, when he didn't respond to the videos of bony-ribbed girls changing clothes next to the toilets, they let him go. These small-town police didn't forget about him, though—they still drove by his little apartment in Shoshone, even after threats from townsfolk kept him from going to the bars and restaurants around town, after he'd purchased a tv and cable so he could drink alone in the darkness of his home. The town itself had a memory too, and after a series of threats from men and women who threw rocks through his front windows, who pounded on his windows and screamed obscenities, he moved his bedroom to a windowless room at the back of the house. Even then, for the next six months the local weekly newspaper filled them in on all the details of his father and what it might have been like to live under his roof, the speculation about father and son ranging wide and far, and for months Parsons found a reporter sleeping in a sedan outside his building. One morning he gathered his courage and brought the reporter coffee because it seemed like something someone in the movies might do—waking up to the person being staked out with a light tapping on the window—the reporter, unwilling to say thanks, poured the coffee out the window on the other side, started his vehicle up and drove off, the snowpack of the street marked like patterns of dance moves over the road dirt.

He could understand the town believing he had the same habits as his old man, but it meant lean times as he tried to do the only job he knew how.

The boy smiled at the woman, placed his hand on Parsons' sleeve, peeked out at the woman, and spoke as if what he had to say would explain everything. "I was practicing my dances downstairs. In the old lady's dance studio. He," the boy said, motioning towards Parsons, "was bagging up old Biscuits, the cat!"

"So you say," the woman said, her eyes moving from the boy to Parsons and back again. "What is this little boy all dressed up for? And why is he here alone with you?" She sucked on her teeth and shook her head when she saw the boy's fingernails as he framed his face with them, making extraordinary mocking expressions as she talked, "You snooping around this little boy here? Pfft."

Parsons wished he hadn't said his name, wished he could just bolt past the woman and out to his van. As it was, the woman had a right to be suspicious. Everyone did, and it made Parsons see it for how everyone else would see it—him alone with a boy in an abandoned house—and in his mind he began to play it like everyone in town would play it: the mirrors, the brass ballet bar, the purple and pink of this weird fucking kid. He regretted touching the brass bar and the mirror now. Fingerprints. A boy and Parsons and a secret dance studio. He nearly laughed with the absurdity of it, the last thing his father had said to him on the last day of his life: *You get photos of the animal from the family. Otherwise you got to hurt em twice when you call for them.* Parsons thinks of the strangeness of that day, the ice dripping from the roof edge so he had to duck, his father adding, *Good to keep it so we have proof they asked for the work.*

"Listen, Ma'am," he said finally. "That was my pop, you're right." The boy had started to tap out a tune next to him, and he reached out and suddenly grabbed Parsons' hand for balance as he tried a new move. The way the boy looked up at him made him sad for everyone. "No one knew about it," he started, then stopped, shed the boy's damp hand from his. Anything he would say would sound incriminating. And it always would. He thinks about what it would have been like to have a father who gave him some small skills of persuasion, something from his childhood to fall back upon, but he could summon nothing of value. After nearly a year, his father's face was harder and harder to summon, and today what came to him was only the image of his leather belt.

The woman was waving over for the boy, trying to extricate him from inside the house, but the boy was busy. The boy grabbed him again, hung on Parsons hand as he let his lithe body swing, toes tapping on the floor then the doorjamb then back and around near Parsons' boots.

"My father," he said, trying to make her understand, "crawled up and over into the dance studio and he put a hunting rifle into his mouth. Did you know that?"

She only had eyes for the boy.

"Sheriff showed me the video," he continued. "Took his head near completely off."

He put his hand on the boy's shoulder to move him forward so she could take him, and the boy spun around, letting her pull him away from Parsons but not before he did a little tap show, one foot set down and his hands up over his head as he clicked and clacked, body nodding back and forth like a sunflower. The boy finished and bowed, said, "Who needs a place to practice if the whole dang world is a studio?"

Parsons thought that was about the smartest thing he'd heard in months, and this small bit of wisdom made him wonder why he had stayed there knowing the long memory of the little town would keep him from ever being more than Jeremiah Parsons' son.

The woman was trying to push the boy behind her back protectively, "You aught'a know you shouldn't be hanging around with no young kids," she said, and he recognized the pattern of the town's discourse with him now. It didn't matter what he said—they acted like they hadn't heard anything he said at all.

"They showed me all of his tapes," he continued. "I had to sit there and look at all they had collected, but you know what? All I could think about was how they could never know what kind of man he was. Not by a long shot."

The woman was holding the boy now, but he squirmed to get away, to dance. She spoke as if she was talking to the boy. "You lucky Ephron aint around to see you creeping. You lucky it was me."

Parsons needed to tell her all of it but couldn't come up with more. "It was illegal. What the Sheriff did," he said. "Wrong, I mean." Parsons switched the bag with the dead cat to his other hand. "I hadn't no love for my father. Heck, he never had love for me neither," he finished.

Parsons knew the boy was going to slip off the porch and into the sharp winter barbs of a rose bush before it happened, everything making so little sense that suddenly it all did. The boy was spinning with his eyes closed and his hands up as if vibrating with the exultations of a fanatic, his feet trap-pap-papping on the icy concrete, and Parsons had a chance to reach out and grab the boy, but he curled his fingers to his chest as if he was protecting his own beating heart. There were things, he realized, that were forbidden to him now. Small things. Like protecting a child from harm, or sitting on the same bench in church, or even attending a sporting event. He felt the cool imprint of the boy's hand on his arm, cool as the barrel of a gun. Even the funeral director had refused to shake his hand, Parsons alone in the room until they carted his father away, and for a moment, the fading touch on his arm felt holy, like a blessing.

He could move away, he thought. Take the business and sell off the old taxidermized heads of animals and bodies of unclaimed family pets; he could pack his vehicle with only his clothing and records and tv and start over. Just the reaching for the boy should not be a sin, he thought, but who else was left to pay for his father's unpaid sins?

The woman wasn't listening to anything he'd said. Her attention was focused on Parsons' face, her hands reaching out behind her to feel for the boy, finding only air in the space the kid had previously occupied, his hands fantastically splayed and still framing his face as he fell backward, his tap shoes scraping and pecking out a staccato rasp on the concrete, and all Parsons could do as the boy began to howl and cry, his blood welling across his exposed arms and through the pink of his thin t-shirt, was close the door behind them both and place his hands on the frame, as if that could hold back all the awful forces that now gathered in the town before him, a boil of all those looking to penalize him for things he cannot explain away.

SHOWN TENDERNESS

A CONVERSATION WITH
SETH BRADY TUCKER

The following conversation was conducted by managing fiction editor James McNulty.

James McNulty: Hey, Seth! Congrats on wrapping up the final draft of "The Taxidermist"! We're excited to publish the story, which was one of the runner-ups for our 2019 Adrift Short Story Contest.

Seth Tucker: Thank you, James and any and all editors at *Driftwood*!

JM: Let's start easy: tell us about the inception and creation of this story.

ST: The concept for this story came to me like many of my stories do: as an initial image or character or situation. In this case it was of a man smoking in a basement with an old boiler ticking alight in the corner. I couldn't 'see' much beyond this initial image, which is the challenge I most love when it comes to the process of writing and inspiration—how the obligation/obsession for me is then founded in my need to discover what the hidden components of the story will be. No roadmap. I love writing like that, love the mystery, that old adage from Robert Frost, "no surprise in the writer, no surprise in the reader" like a metronome in the background of the work. The story itself came out in one fell swoop, the language and imagery and scenes all boiling up as if from some dark hyper-conscious place as if it had been waiting, preformed, for me to mine it out of those strange pre-memories. On a good writing day, that is what it feels like to me: a bit mystical and

ordained. Writers get lucky sometimes with stories that appear out of the ether as if we are simply transcribing words from the spirit world. It left me panting and tired and I left it alone for a couple months so I could return to it fresh and without expectations so my re-Vision of it would be un-muddied.

JM: When it comes to revision, how does the "mysticism" of the original drafting process play in? Do you go to the same "hyper-conscious" place, or does revision bring in more rigorous logic? If the latter, how do you walk the balance between honoring the mystery and cleaning up the work?

ST: I don't want to make it all sound like I subscribe to some hippy-dippy belief in 'stories from space' or some nonsense like that, but I find that when I am trying to explain how it feels the language just naturally gravitates to the mystical. I've learned to love both the generative moments of a story or poem as much as I love the re-Visioning of a piece. That wasn't always the case; in grad school I fell into the bad habit of just cranking a story out and then not touching it again. I think that I just liked the feeling of having a quick win but I hadn't learned to commit to the whole process. So, to answer your question: I try to find the best form of the story by breaking down the story or poem into parts. It is actually a very practical process where I have faith (or I try to) in the material but am open to changes that will raise the tension or help with momentum and character and story. I rarely think of plot in the traditional sense (I save that for the novel-writing). Revising this story helped me to understand the woman on the porch would be critical for the final moments (the first draft was more reliant on just a scene with the boy and Parsons). Editing is the most trying part of the process, so I was thankful to have your deep edits for this piece, and I feel the story is much improved due to your help!

JM: Of course! We work through the same process with all our writers—even the contest winners. The hope is that we can give the writers something more lasting than just money or something to slap on their cover letter; as long as the editor isn't too demanding, it can only be a beneficial process, albeit time-consuming.

I don't think you're off-base in your terminology. Most writers describe generation in abstract terms; what I find interesting personally is the marriage of the two, which comes through more clearly in revision (as well as in the writer/editor coupling). Talk to me a little bit about the word you keep using: not *revision* but *re-Vision*. I've always considered the five types of drafting: outlining, generation, rewriting, revision, and editing. It seems like your "re-vision" is similar to my "rewriting." Is that correct?

ST: The way I think of re-Vision is more the entirety of the writing process and a way to communicate to my students how true revision happens over time and from the ground up—and editing is really the last turn of a long and curvy road. The generation of the material is often the fulfilling and fun part for beginning writers so it is where they often stop. I have known a handful of truly gifted writers through my teaching, and I can only think of one who committed to the idea of 'whole earth' revision (and it is why they are still writing and successful). So I would classify my own approach as: generation, re-Vision, and editing—with editing itself being the last and (hopefully) least critical of the three. That isn't to say editing is not crucial—the hope is that by the time I send it out it is

mostly finished with the line-by-line editing simply because I have 'heard' it out loud enough times to have fixed most the problems—it gets a bit more tricky with characters with big voices, or narrators with big voices, of course.

So, to simplify: my conception of re-Vision is one that allows me to anticipate and see issues within my stories because I am revising for structure, scene, image, etc., as I go (and yes, this means sometimes I will go through and completely restructure a piece, then go back and work on scene-by-scene momentum, then a revision might have me expanding the world the characters occupy, and then it might be a revision that has me compressing language and scene as I go paragraph-by-paragraph). I have a list of ten strategies that I might employ in a revision, each of them moved back or forward in importance as I go and as the story demands. Sometimes we get lucky with a story and it just works with very little revision, but I think that has happened maybe ten times in my life and across three genres. The art is really in what we do with it after we've carved out the initial idea.

JM: All makes sense to me. One clarification: why does it "get more tricky with characters with big voices"?

ST: What I mean is that the more voice-driven or more powerful the speaker's voice is in a piece, the harder it is to edit line-by-line in a serious grammatical manner (the way I might correct student essays). Odd syntax often communicates voice, idiosyncratic grammar can punch up how we hear a character or narrator and how we 'learn' to hear them. That gets tricky when it is time to sit down and form the piece into a shape that can and will get published, and sometimes that voice we hear is actually getting in the way of the actual story. I think some of that was actually happening with "The Taxidermist" in my early drafts because Parsons is not necessarily a story-teller and he is not functioning fully in the world he is seeing/narrating.

JM: And what, if you don't mind summarizing them quickly for our readers, are your ten strategies for re-vision?

ST: I am happy to give you my list, but I lied about the ten—it is more like fifteen—and they get rotated out as the demands for each story change, so I've highlighted the ones I specifically remember using for "The Taxidermist." You will surely recognize the one focused on tense. In the end, for some stories I may only use a handful, but I often go down this list to see if anything pops out at me.

I would say that the three critical revision strat-egies I use almost every time, for every story, are: (1) Considering the POV/tense; (2) Mapping it out; (3) Reading it out loud/rewriting it completely. I know that when you saw my first revision, I had tried (and mostly failed) to use present tense, and during the second revision, I know that I mapped it out and re-examined how the flashbacks and side-cuts were working, which ultimately led to a change in the orga-nization of the story.

Seth Tucker's Revision Checklist

1. Structural concerns. Is the order of events in its best and necessary order? What happens if pieces are moved?
2. Time management. Is this a story that demands quick momentum for the reader, or a slower pace, or a mix? Examine each paragraph and scene for pacing. Compress or expand as needed.
3. POV. What kind of story is this and is it being told in the best and most logical way and through the best narrative voice?
4. Rewrite this story (does it need/deserve it?) by hand or by re-typing it. Try to be open to big changes as you go.
5. Destroy abstractions. Do a word search for "it," "this," "that," "those," "its," "they," "them," "thing(s)," "he," "her," etc. Do another word search for overused words.
6. Who is necessary? Whose story is this? Cut characters who can have what they bring to the story repurposed or taken on by other characters.
7. Tense. Does the current address work, and is it possible to learn what we must learn in this iteration? Shift tense if needed.
8. The cave. Go back into what James Dickey called "the cave of making" with your characters (this works sometimes and sometimes not) and look for those moments that might be over written when they could be clear, concise, and true.
9. Read it out loud.
10. Map it out. Take the piece scene-by-scene and examine carefully whether each scene is doing what it needs to. Is it necessary? Can what it is doing be moved or added elsewhere?
11. See the story. Draw scenes if possible (my novel was mapped out like an FBI investigator tack-board at one point). What cannot be drawn is likely to remain unseen by the reader.
12. Put it away for a couple months if you need to. See it fresh. Revise again.
13. Address. Is the story being told by and through the correct person—is the complicated mix of narrative distance, psychic distance, and POV serving the needs of the story?
14. Simplify. Cut academic or over-written passages or break them down into their simplest forms (this has been something I've had to do more as I've spent more time in academia).
15. No one needs your bullshit. This story is about these characters, so are there aspects where you have injected yourself into the story?

JM: The organizational revision worked wonderfully, I think. When it came to moving the story into present tense, however, I remember something odd happened: it seemed to suck the story of its mysticism, of the slight surrealism. The tone changed completely—simply because of a tense change. Ultimately, you agreed and moved the story back to past tense. What do you think happened there?

All of those revision techniques sound exceptionally useful, by the way; I hope our readers—most of whom are fellow writers—copy them down.

ST: I think so too, and I'm very happy with what we are bringing to *Driftwood*. I think the momentum and tension is much improved in the latest version. It is interesting what the 'practice' of writing, what revision and the manipulation of certain craft approaches can do to a work, and it is something I try to communicate in class about tone: I think one of the problems with deep revision is that sometimes the writer can lose focus or lose the thread of what makes a story tick. In the case of "The Taxidermist," I think what happened was that I was in the middle of shifting the tense of my novel and had a moment where it just seemed to make sense that we, the reader, should experience Parsons' life immediately and at the same time he does. It seemed like a no-brainer, but once it was in that form, I agree—the oddity of the story was normalized, as if this sort of stuff happens to Parsons all the time—and that lack of mystery and strangeness deeply impacted the tone that I'd set in earlier drafts. I like to think of this as part of that 'practice,' I mentioned, that learning process that is at the heart of all writing. Richard Bausch once wrote, "I don't teach writing. I teach patience. Toughness. Stubbornness. The willingness to fail." I very much subscribe to this.

JM: Right. A seemingly simple—yet fundamental—craft decision such as tense can change the entirety of the story—and how it's read. I can also vouch for your point about the danger of losing tone in revisions; I've seen far too many revisions come back to me where the writer had clearly lost sight of the bones of the story after having been away from it for too long. Of course, most times this can be beneficial to a writer—

this time apart and changing up the bones—but in our case, if a story has made it far enough to be selected for the critiquing phase, it probably doesn't need so significant a shift.

One of the things we spent time on in our back-and-forth was how physical intimacy worked in the story; you pushed that there should be more of it leading up to the end. Could you talk a little bit about how the physicality of the child affects Parsons—especially in your spot-on conclusion?

ST: Parsons is a man who has completely lost his sense of 'true north' even though his compass was attuned to the broken figure of his father—an immoral man, a man with no tenderness, etc.—and when I first began to think about what it is that Parsons wants, what he yearns for, it came to me that it must be some simple form of physical or emotional contact. In the story, he has essentially gone untouched for over a year (we are led to believe that he has been assaulted, but that should add to, rather than subtract from, that isolation), so when the boy reaches for him, he doesn't know how to react to it. Those final pages should have the reader thinking that the best and worst thing that could happen is for the boy and Parsons to show each other some tenderness through physical touch (and especially to do it in front of this very suspicious woman). It is ultimately why I have them come into contact with one another, but also to make it very dissatisfying for Parsons (and hopefully uncomfortable for the reader). Of course, there is so much emotional compression happening in those moments, that each reader (as final collaborator on any written piece) can have a satisfactory read on what it means to Parsons and his place in this world.

JM: One of our new editors, Stephen Hundley, shot over a few questions for the interview. Here's one of them: "Taxidermy and dance language permeate this piece. In the hands of a less thoughtful or careful author, this might feel shoehorned. How do you go about integrating theme into scene?"

ST: This is a great question and it got me thinking about the nature of scene building, how it is done, how I specifically do it, and how theme is built over time. The short answer is that I don't really think about theme until there is something that presents itself as theme-worthy as I discover what bears weight in a story, and I cannot think of a story I've written in the last decade that has had thematic elements that I have purposefully placed in an initial draft. This isn't to say that I don't deeply consider how all the images or scenes or details will stack up, but rather how much attention the reader should give them. Theme is truly measured by the amount of attention or devotion a writer gives to the details that 'reflect' on the theme. Motif works on that same principle but there might be a lesser degree of focus, and then to an even lesser degree we just get details about the world or characters (and these may still function as objective correlatives). Placement and focus are the key. Like it is a light shining on reflective pieces the author has placed throughout a piece. Those pieces of 'reflective material' we place in a story might rise to theme, or might present as motif, or to a lesser extent they might just become recognizable details that carry some unique purpose. I think that in the grand depleting scale of theme-motif-details, the studio in "The Taxidermist" might be more motif than theme, but I agree—there is something slippery there—I think that the dancing, the studio, the bronze bars hidden in the basement reside somewhere in-between what my conception of theme and motif are. I absolutely wanted the reader to feel the tension of these haunted places as we went along, wanted the reader to know that underneath it all, children are dancing and it is the tapping of their feet that imperil Parsons like some awful pace-maker. These should reflect, refract, shine so that the reader knows that the innocence of Parsons and the boy is centrally part of the problem. They are in spiritual danger, and the reader should worry for them.

JM: For the most part, I like your idea of how themes operate here; particularly useful is your idea of placement and levels of focus. The best way, it seems to me, to get themes across is via moments of focus, intuitive placement, motifs, and objective correlatives, as you say. What's the alternative? I have read far too many submissions where the characters, the narrator,

or the interiority directly speaks about the themes, rather than letting them come through more naturally in the way you describe. That said, if you're thinking about objective correlatives, motifs, placements, and stresses, then clearly you're thinking about themes— and I'm willing to bet some of this thought occurs during the generation. As you discover themes while writing, your conscious or subconscious will tend to lean into those discoveries as you continue to write. When you say you don't think about theme during the drafting, you just mean you don't *begin* the draft with a targeted theme, right? Or do you really mean that there's zero thought about theme (placements, stresses, motifs, etc.) during your first drafting?

ST: You are right: I'm not making plans around some larger thematic set-piece, and only really do when it is presented to me as I write. This goes back to that effort to discover as I write, rather than to plot out ahead of time, what I plan to do. Let's take the two studios for example: the one next to his father's shop became necessary once I had fleshed out the scene in the basement. Once those bronze bars appeared, I knew that I needed an image or motif that would create a linkage between the tension with the boy and the trauma of his father's suicide. I recognized the need immediately, but it wasn't originally what I thought the story would be about. When this happens, and it doesn't always, it makes me feel like I have suddenly recognized a familiar and beloved face in a crowd. It's probably why I keep coming back, time after time.

JM: Another question from Stephen: "How does dance operate in this story? It's proximate to suspected sexual violence and voyeurism, yet also with play and innocence. In your mind, what does making dance central contribute to the difficult position that Parsons finds himself in? Likewise for taxidermy: with very little Taxidermy in the actual story, why choose this profession for Parsons?"

ST: Hmmm. I may have partially answered this in a previous questions, but let me dive a bit deeper. I think you are dead-on with your instincts and you recognize that the dancing of the boy is meant to be innocent and playful. The structure of the story was deliberately around that sweetness in the boy, how he is teaching Parsons to live free and in the moment, but because we already know of the crimes committed by his father, everything after that scene takes on a sinister tone. I don't want our readers to worry that the son (Jeremy Parsons) is following in the footsteps of the father, but I do want them to worry over it, to have to turn it over and over as we go, examining how all these connections matter, how they communicate back and forth, how the details of the world reflect on that shiny moment at the end of the story when he tries to close the world out behind a thin door. The surreal nature of the story adds to this effect, I think, and allows the reader to believe that anything is possible in this little strange world.

The fact that Parsons is both a taxidermist and a pest-control goes back to the first couple of hours I spent on this story: one of the first images I had was of a man in a basement smoking a cigarette, and the second was of a man pulling hide up over a deer mold. That second image didn't make it into the story, but the vision of a man struggling with thick hide was spinning up as I was writing the story. I have some experience with this as the son of a mountain guide (my father is a rancher and guide in Wyoming, so I spent most of my childhood with hunters and ranch-hands), so I think the memories of elk and antelope and mountain sheep hanging bloody in our garage might have something to do with that, but I also thought it was a pretty good symbol for what Parsons is going through: he is trying to find the mold that he can stretch his life over, but with no luck, so he just keeps going, placing one hopeless foot in front of the other in the belief that the solution will present itself.

JM: You mentioned the "surreal nature of the story." How do you enact surrealism craft-wise? That is to say, give our readers some strategies for employing the tone as well as you have. We've so far discovered that writing in past tense helps. Have you noticed anything about your sentence structures that have changed when leaning into surrealism? Or is it all in the details—what you choose to say and highlight?

ST: Most of my stories tend to lean toward the strange or odd, but I'm not unique in that given the fact that it is the fiction writer's job to recreate world, and how demanding that job now, to 'strange' our current world? Sometimes it feels like I am writing creative nonfiction! I think you are right—it is absolutely in the details and the images and what a writer has us focus our eye and ear on. I think, for instance, that the boy in my story would be wholly changed, the tone wholly changed, if I had put him in Wranglers and a dirty t-shirt. His preciousness is part of his allure, part of his peculiarity, those carefully painted nails, the angelic pink and white and *cleanliness* of the boy matter most in the long run. After all, he is doing nothing out of the ordinary, right? He's eating Cheerios, playing the way all children play, exploring in the way all children explore, and in the end, there is nothing truly odd about Parsons either—just a man trying to get through another awful day, lonely—and looking for something else. There is a wonderful story by Mark Strand entitled "Space" that does this perfectly, I think. In it (and this will not ruin the story for the readers, by the way, because great literature works even when you already know how it will end), a man arrives on the top of a building in NY and sees a woman about to jump. He tries to save her in all the idiotic ways a man tries to save a woman: first by telling her he understands, then that he will take her away from it all, that he will marry her, etc., but the details, the *details* are about what the man sees. And he cannot stop looking at her body, at how she is dressed, at how she holds herself, at her buttocks. It is one of the great pieces of flash-fiction, truly. Sorry for that aside. So yes, it is all about what you teach your reader to focus their reading eye on as they move through a piece (and I think this works in poetry as well—in Forche's "The Colonel," for instance, sound and what is heard are primary to the details and images, and then we learn it is because the colonel will dump a bag of ears on the table and all those glittering pieces explode as they reflect that light). Again, that poem will not be ruined by knowing how it ends! Ultimately, what the writer chooses to highlight and stress will do the work, if we are brave enough to trust it.

JM: Unconventional sentence structures would help too, I suspect. Anything that makes the writing feel just a smite *off*; surrealism comes almost entirely from the unexpected. Anything surreal will not be expected; it's similar to comedy in that way. I've just been watching now—for the first time—the reboot of *Twin Peaks*, and it's been a ton of fun to see how full-on, no-holds-barred surrealism works in that show. Lynch pushes as far as he can into the unexpected without ever (or rarely, perhaps) getting too far away from the narrative for the surrealism to be superfluous. When compared to Lynch, your story is certainly on the lite side of surreal, but I think it operates on the same principles. The focuses and stresses you talk about are unexpected to the reader, and that gives them the sense that something is *off*, or surreal.

On a nitty-gritty craft level, I suspect moving the story to present tense brought the attention more to the verbs—which become much more active and grabbing in present tense—and that took the attention away from the other stresses that the more subtle past tense was able to better highlight.

ST: I think so too, and our back and forth with editing sometimes moved into the 'how and why' of each line (in a good way) because sometimes I can let the poetic side of my sensibilities run amok. So it wasn't enough for strange things to be happening to Parsons, but the story had to *sound* off too—and that was why having Parsons in some control through third-person limited was so necessary, and why he often wasn't the best at telling his own story. I wanted the reader to feel like they were learning at the exact same rate as Parsons (and also another reason why I thought trying present tense might work). That's the process. One of the things I liked about the present tense was how the story sounded for the reader, but I totally agree that this then made us focus our eye on the wrong aspects of the details and world as we went along.

JM: Stephen had one more question that asks about something I wanted to talk in more detail about: the ending. Here it is: "Can you speak to the ending of this piece? Parsons pressing his hands against the door frame seems to be a gesture of futility. The characters seems more entrenched in his difficult situation than ever."

ST: Yes, ultimately, I just couldn't figure out a clean exit where the story would be served (or the reader, for that matter) with anything that went beyond that moment on the porch, how the conflicts from there will likely escalate, how Parsons would get out of this or succumb to the pressures and prejudices of the town, how the boy will come out of it unscathed and whether this town is going to try to change him too. Not a very optimistic ending, I'm afraid, but I do hope the reader is able to see the new clench to Parsons' jaw, his willingness now to consider what changes must happen, etc. I hope that the boy teaches us something even as he teaches Parsons something—the courage it takes to chase dreams and to dance in the front of these empty spaces—of course, I don't believe that Parsons has the strength to shake himself awake, but maybe the reader will see some angle they had not considered before.

JM: I particularly loved the ending because of the cyclicality of it all, the almost catch-22: the townsfolk thinking he'll hurt a child causes him to allow a child to be hurt. Parsons could've reached out his hand, but he chooses not to because of how he's been wronged—and because of the insecurities and fears that the wronging caused. I think it's good to end on this note, alongside the somewhat clear indication that Parsons has resolved—if he can get out of his current situation—to finally move to a new town. Your ending goes out on a high note—a moment of tension—rather than quickly de-escalating the tensions and ending with a whimper. I'm not so sure there's a question amongst the praise there, but here's one, just to see if I can get you to answer it: Who the hell called Parsons out there?

ST: Thank you for your kind words! I am certainly happy that this story landed with *Driftwood* and I landed in some good company with the winner and other finalists. I know that 'the call' remains a mystery and the only answer I have to that is this: the story would have exploded, would have gone from ~3,000 words to 6,000+ words with the expansion of the world around Parsons. In the end, I liked that mystery, that sense that this could have been some cruel prank, or worse. But my concern with a conspiracy by the townsfolk is that then that would demand quite a bit of contextualizing and back-story, and I liked the quietness of this piece. I think that would have been broken by any additional 'players.'

JM: All agreed. The mystery also adds to the tone, and it isn't very important to the narrative to have it answered.

You mentioned Mark Strand and Forche earlier. What other writers have influenced your writing—and "The Taxidermist" in particular?

ST: I love questions about influences, but these are always the hardest to answer: who hasn't influenced my writing? Some authors seem to be perennially teaching me, while others shine bright and leave me breathless and make me want to try some strategy that they have mastered. So in no particular order: Adam Johnson (he was a schoolmate of mine), Margaret Atwood, David Kirby (poet and mentor) taught me to take risks. Rebecca Makkai, Ralph Ellison, and Jesmyn Ward (recently read all her books in a week, then read them again) taught me how to manage pacing. Paul Beattie is probably the writer who most impacted my sense of oddity and isolation in Parsons world, and his satirical novels are the best we have seen since Heller. Recently, Jasmin Darznik's writing has gut-punched me emotionally, so I know I've looked to her work to help understand how pathos is built, even for characters who might seem ethically challenged. But I could go through the 1000+ books I own and probably find a number of things in all of them that have impacted my writing in some way or another.

JM: How about other mediums? Film? Music? Art? What else has most influenced you?

ST: Terry Gilliam! I've probably watched *12 Monkeys* twenty times. I like the impossible worlds he creates (*Time Bandits*) and the complex plot and movement of his movies like *12 Monkeys* and then the surrealism and pacing of *The Fisher King* and *Brazil* et al. This penchant for spelunking the strange might be something that has been with me a very long time—I was raised in a poor community and went to a pretty terrible public school, so I wasn't exactly well-versed in the arts early on—but I remember being pulled in quickly by the visual wonders of Dali and Edvard Munch and other surrealists and my musical tastes have always leaned toward the avant garden and alternative blends. It might just be that I want the world to be more wonderfully strange, so am always looking for those who tell that story best in their art. It is a bit more difficult to define my musical inspirations simply because I love music so much, but my favorites who tend to show up Spotify playlists are songwriters like Brandi Carlisle, John Prine, Benjamine Fitzsimmons, Glen Hansard, and many other story-tellers.

JM: Gilliam is always fun; for some reason, it's *Parnassus* that has stuck with me most—perhaps just because of how innovative they were in recasting Ledger after his death mid-production—though I think *Fisher King* is probably Gilliam's best. It's been years since I've seen any of them, so I'm probably off-mark. And, yeah, I think most *Driftwood* contributors are into the avant garde—be it in writing, music, art, or film. Our sensibilities here tend to lean that way—while also valuing narrative higher than the average experimentalist, which sets us in this nice middle-ground: a fertile ground for publishing stories like yours and others.

Let's wrap up this interview by looking to the future. What projects are you working on now?

ST: I'll have to check out *Parnassus* again. Right now, I am in the middle of a pretty major overhaul of a novel I started five years ago. One of the dangers of being a writer who discovers versus a writer who plots is that at one point in the writing of the novel (which is entitled *The Baptisms of Albert Shoe*), it was almost 700 pages long. I've whittled that down to around 400, but there is still some fine-tuning that needs to be done. My hope is that my agent will be ready to take it to publishers this year. While I've been hard at work at that, I've also completed a poetry manuscript that is out there in some publishers hands and from whom I hope to hear back soon, and due to the recent stay-at-home order, I've been forced to face a handful of short stories that I know need work. I'm hopeful, and I am very, very thankful that the Colorado School of Mines was already preparing for online instruction (and had given me the resources ahead of time to easily transition). I am acutely aware of how fortunate I am to be able to do something I love (teaching and writing) while all this is going on.

JM: At the time of this interview, we're in the thick of it, so it's hard to have any sort of perspective. That said, what do you think the lasting change will be in the literary community post-COVID19?

ST: I don't think I have any sense of what might happen once this is over, once we emerge from this pandemic and into a world forever changed, but here's what I hope happens: I hope that we all come away with a new devotion and loyalty to our essential workers, that we band together to pay all full-time workers a living wage, that we realize that healthcare is an essential human right, that we elevate our teachers and police and firefighters and nurses and all those careers we now recognize as critical to our nation and people. I hope we can see it clearly now, that we can recognize how non-essential our politicians and CEOs and pop heroes really are and how artists and creators are what we turn to when the shit really hits the fan. I hope that in the coming weeks and months the sudden shift in how we see K-12 and secondary educators maintains this good momentum, that we cherish these heroes by paying them. But more than that: I hope we can remember to love one another in spite of our politics, that we can get back to being citizens who care for each and every person drawing breath in the country. Personally, I think the first step toward a better USA has just happened—for the first time in generations, we have asked the average citizen to sacrifice—and many and most have risen to the task. That devotion to a common good is hard to ignore, I believe.

JM: It's good to hear that optimism right now. Politically speaking, I'm not so optimistic, but I hope all of the movements that you note here happen—and more.

I think that about wraps everything up, Seth. Thanks for taking the time to work through this interview in these troubling times. Is there anything else you'd like to leave us with—about "The Taxidermist" or writing in general?

ST: The only truly helpful advice I can give is one of persistence: writers should always try to remember that this is not work, but play. Try to remember those days on the playground, perhaps a moment when you were kicking a ball around and there was no expectation of rewards or recognition. It was the experience that mattered. Keep that purity in your heart, and the work will become the play and the play will turn into production and that will nearly always bring a writer to joy. For readers: buy books from local bookstores and offer to review the books you love!

GEOFFREY DETRANI'S RENDITION GARDEN

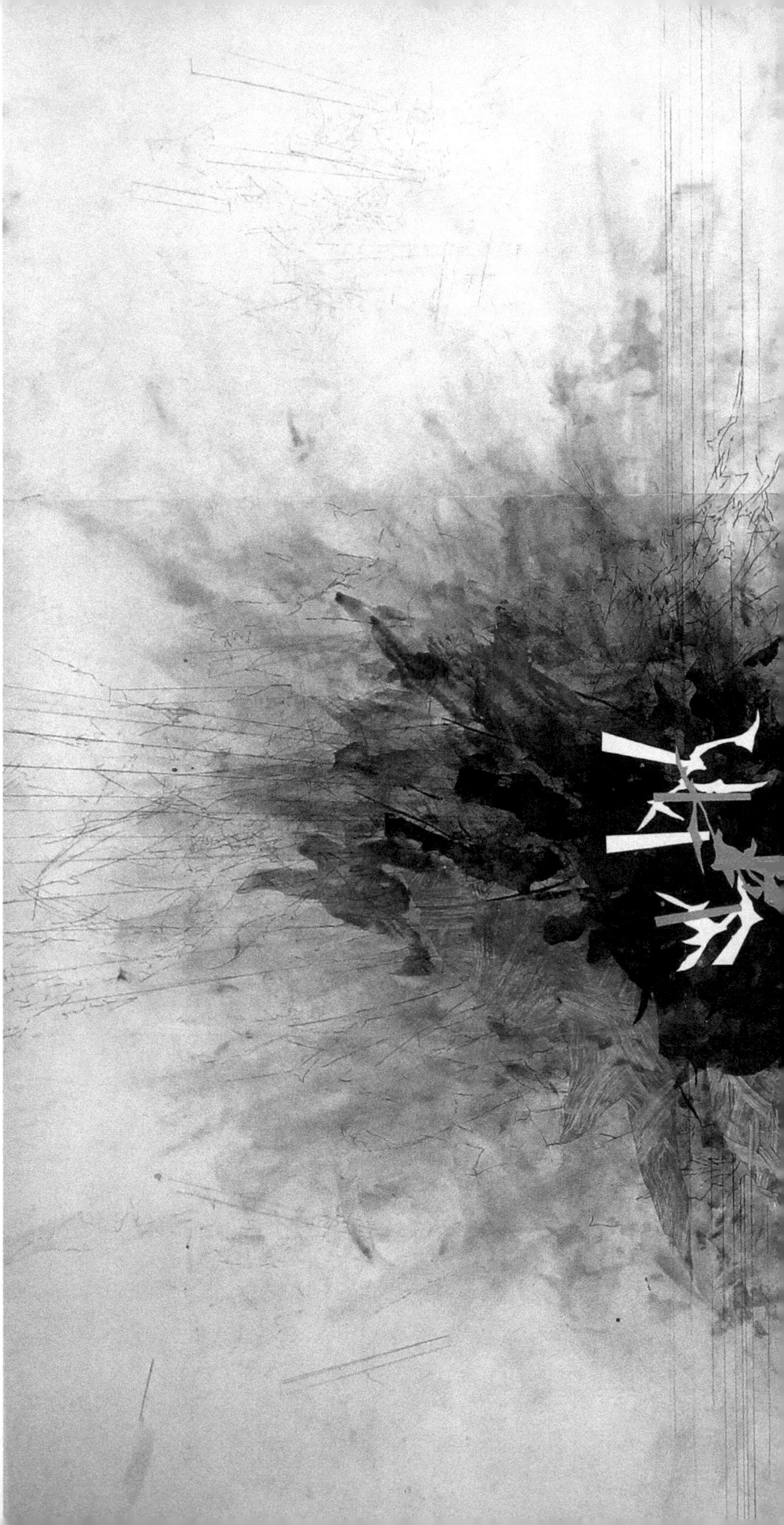

GEOFFREY DETRANI'S
STALEMATE COSMOLOGY

GEOFFREY DETRANI'S
TROPHIES TREATIES

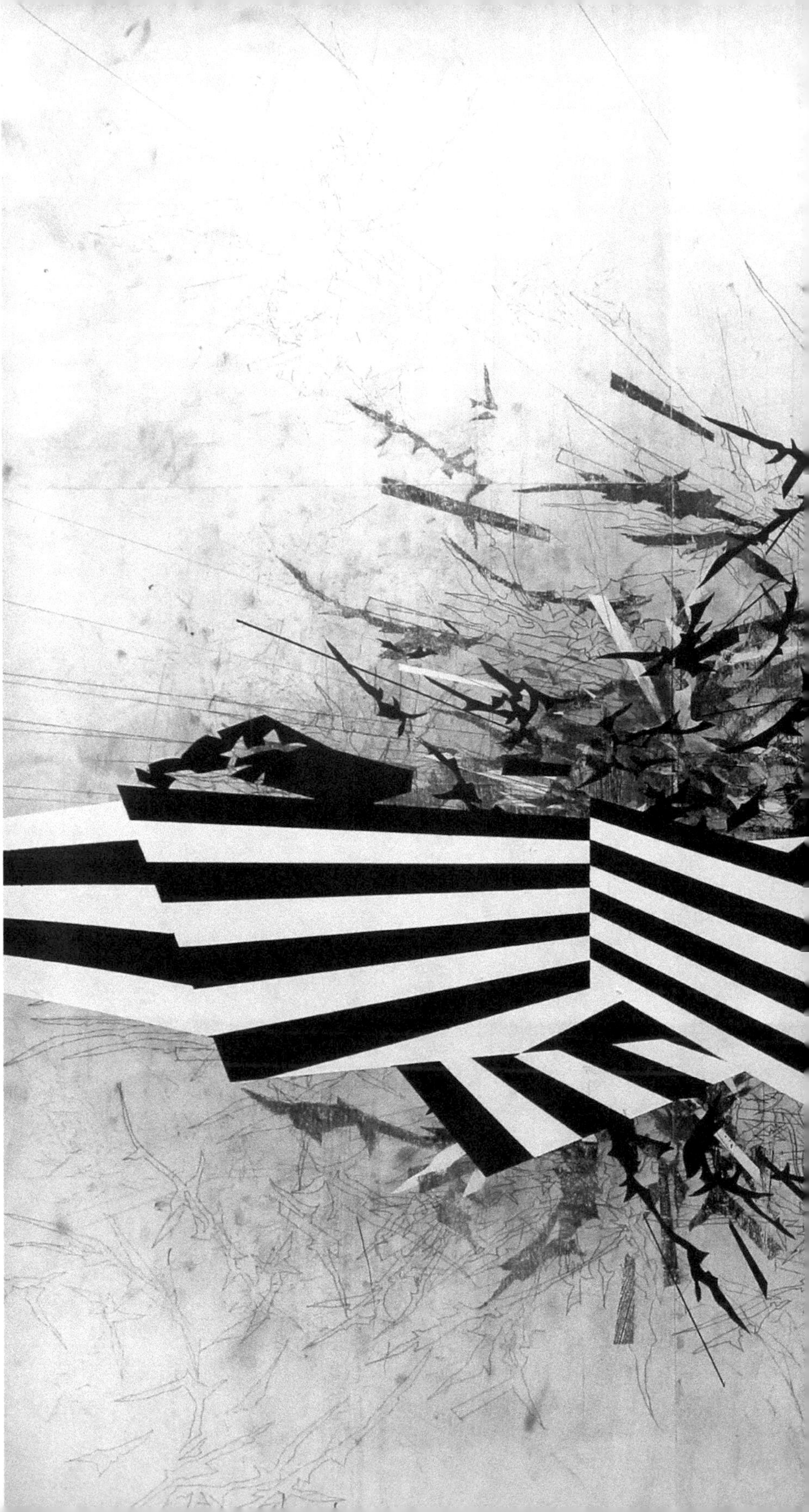

EVERY TIME I GO BACK IS ENCODED IN PI

ANNIE CHRISTAIN

"I'd be interested in doing a reversal but also being allowed to remember what happens now."
-Shelley Duvall, Dr. Phil interview

She puts her blood on a Severus Snape poster again; I gain entry by remembering her miasma pattern and how it vibrates to my theme. This is why I'm related to her son, but not genetically. The other wives who know better call her a fool,

but I will always be her conservator.

She reminds me she's not a lesbian and asks me to withdraw from the Holy Tree Grid so we can manifest the life forms we prefer. She asks me to parasitize her pneuma—*in those exact words.*

Other life forms appear, and they only show up to watch me pin her down in her own soul-webbing I stripped and sewed together throughout my lifetimes. The long game.

I turn the crank on the alien machinery; I join her on a higher artificial plane as her master. I rock her through the internal explosions. She remembers we have always been this.

I am in her and her in me.

When she cries in the kitchen, I encourage her to buy more dishtowels and chicken thigh family packs; when she has an earache, I push down on her neck so the exercises can relieve the pressure. I correct her when she tries to use a sink plunger in the toilet.

When she tells me she can't concentrate on me, I ask her what she thought would happen when she brought authentic wardrobe patches from *The Vampire Diaries* into this house.

I watch her and make her prove to me she's not stupid.

A man who claims he's not gay because he only *receives* blowjobs from other men could be right, but not for that reason.

I am her false Snape in a female body, but where she and I are encoded in pi makes this a true religion.[1]

---

[1]"So when [Akira Haraguchi] learned that pi is an endless series of numbers with no pattern or repetition, it made perfect sense to him to take it as a symbol of life, he says—adding that he now calls pi memorization 'the religion of the universe.'" "How can anyone remember 100,000 numbers?" by Tomoko Otake, *the japan times*, 12/17/06

INTERVIEW
WITH ANNIE CHRISTAIN

First, let me start by saying how much we loved this poem! It is rife with specific details, mysteries, and hints to a larger discourse on relationships and bodies that make this poem echo long past it's last line. I wanted to start our interview by diving into the epigraph and footnote of the poem. Did you always intend to bookend the poem with these? What do you think are the benefits of adding these elements to a poem?

I'm really glad I had the chance to participate in such an outstanding poetry contest!

The epigraph and footnote help me as a writer to enter and stay in a certain framework to generate ideas, like a prompt I'm responding to. Duvall's line about wanting to do a "reversal" made me think of taking that idea literally…having a speaker who had the ability to keep traveling back in time to experience and perfect a relationship while remembering all of her previous attempts.

The Akira Haraguchi quote is perfect because it combines pi and religion, and my poem contains Christian allusions and references to Snapewives, women who engage in romantic relationships with Snape through other women who channel him as a form of a fiction-based religion.

In Tiana Clark's interview in divedapper she described epigraphs as conversations poets have with those who came before. I thought, Yes! Epigraphs let the reader know where they're entering your poetic conversation you're having with someone else.

I always love a poem that plays with form, and "Every Time I Go Back Is Encoded in Pi" seems to tease at the strengths of a prose poem, while keeping the explosive power of a few short lines and focused breaks. What did the visual language look like in its first draft?

In the first draft, I developed a beginning, middle, and end (conjuring, intimacy, fallout) that was more straightforward and serious.

It took me a while to settle on terms like "Holy Tree Grid" and "pneuma," words that add a religious/mystical punch and are unusual. Then I wove humor in.

A lot of times my prose poems start out as one chunk. In this poem "I will always be her conservator," "I am in her and her in me," and "I watch her and make her prove to me she's not stupid" reveal authoritarian character traits of the speaker and provide clues as to why the relationship never works and needs to be "redone" over and over. That's why I wanted those lines to stand out more on the page.

There are many standout lines in this work, but the one that captured me the most was the intensity of "I am in her and her in me" that appears midway through. There is a quiet assurance here that echoes Adrienne Rich's proclamation "I am she: I am he" from her seminal poem "Diving into the Wreck". What was the hardest part about writing this expression of bodies and their relationship to one another? What was the easiest?

I like the connection you made to Rich's poem. My line was inspired by John 17:23. "I in them, and You in Me; that they may be made perfect in one…" The easiest part of writing that line was that it needed no revisions, and I wrote it instantly after writing the previous line. The hardest part was deliberating on whether or not the wording or syntax was too close to the original, but then I was like, oh yeah, even if it's similar, mine's about lesbians so I've made it my own.

In terms of the expression of bodies and their relationship to one another, I like that on one level the line expresses the most basic and literal way to express a sexual act, and on another with its religious associations, the line also hints that the relationship is getting too heavy and going too far, especially since the speaker's modus operandi is spiritual possession. So the expression of bodies and their relationship to one another as expressed in the line shows more of an overreaching than a connection, full of dangers and the unknown, like Billy Pilgrim discovering that so much of sexual reproduction takes place in the invisible fourth dimension.

Much of this poem exists in an intensely first-person point of view, and all of those I's draw us very close into your own perceptions and actions. Did you struggle with this level of insight into your life? Is there such a thing as having 'too close' of a view in a poem?

From the close view I take in the poem, I can ask myself, "Does my quest for perfectionism hurt myself and others due to the lengths I'm willing to go to achieve my goals?" "Do I sabotage relationships because I'm selfish and want to be treated like God?" As poets, we have to be self-aware and let the poem move in the direction it's supposed to move in, even if doing so reminds us we can be jerks IRL. The close view becomes too close when the reader has no room to participate in the question/answer self-discovery, life-discovery process.

The inclusion of pi, a number that has no end, adds a whole other level of complexity here, and as an editor it's refreshing to see a mathematical concept approached through the lens of poetry. Was pi crucial to this poem, or did this aspect come later?

Daniel Tammet has been a big inspiration on my writing. He has a private mathematical language and visually experiences pi in shapes with rich textures and colors. His inner world of synesthesia and living numbers shows the complex, beautiful structures that could exist in things that we're told only have one function of purpose. As a writer, I went in with the idea, okay, how about we say pi is a timeline we can hop around on when we can access it in 3D, and in numeric form pi is the record of our journeys? "The religion of the universe." Researching other people's unique forms of perception has made it easier for me to ask these kinds of questions that aid me in my writing.

More to that point, how much revision went into this poem?

I spent about a full month revising this poem. I did a lot of fine-tuning—looking for the perfect descriptions, working to layer the poem in scenes and images that transcend the fantasy genre without the whole poem collapsing in on itself. Finding that balance took some time to achieve.

Is this poem categorical of your work? Why or why not?

It's my first Harry Potter poem, but it won't be my last! The synthesis found in the poem is typical of my work. Usually I write a poem by setting out to combine three or more unlike things to see how they could possibly fit, sort of as a personal challenge and in order to keep my writing fresh. This poem is research-based too like most of my poems, and I seek out unusual content for inspiration: conspiracy YouTube videos and comments, police interrogations archived on true crime websites, articles or self-published books that people discount. Actually the Snapewives phenomenon has been ridiculed online, but I wanted to research it with an open mind, to put myself in the wives' positions and see if there's something there that the public is missing that could be intriguing for a poem.

If you had to narrow it down, what three books have had the most impact on your writing?

Matilda by Roald Dahl made me want to be a writer when I was a kid.

Year of the Snake by Lee Ann Roripaugh blew my mind and made me want to be a poet in practice and not just in my head.

Dakota Days by John Green went against official media stances and made me want to venture into speculative fiction.

APPRIATE JEWELS FOR COURTSHIP

EMILY PAIGE WILSON

Imagine a blood clot, proper and pompous. Long as language and its elaborate shadow. Treasonous and terrycloth, the towels. Best to wed on a Wednesday, if the clot is caught in the lungs.

Moonstone:

> Ghost in glass, thin clasp of gold.
> Coldly confident and floating.

Amethyst:

> To be middle class is to be royal.
> To be royal is to worry always
> what the servants will say.

Pearl:

> My mother died before I learned
> how to be impolite. She'll be buried
> in her beloved luster of propriety.
> How pleased she'll be—see her
> sheen, sometimes pink, sometimes green.

Opal:

> Three children crying together
> are a stream. One child crying
> alone is an ocean—open and mean.

Best to wed on a Sunday if a cough cannot explain the clot.

INTERVIEW
WITH EMILY PAIGE WILSON

What inspired the poem?

This poem is part of a manuscript-in-progress: a poetic biography of Marie Lafarge based on her memoirs. In 1840, Lafarge became the first person to be convicted of murder through the use of forensic toxicology. She was accused of feeding her husband arsenic. Her story is fantastically wild. It contains a marriage borne of false circumstances, stolen jewels, a poisoned fruitcake, and dueling chemists.

What was the hardest part about writing it?

The most challenging aspect of this piece and the project in general is crafting the appropriate voice and tone. Lafarge maintains her innocence, but is she a reliable narrator? Either she's an innocent woman who was wrongly convicted; a guilty woman who could have been justified in her actions because of the abuse and manipulation she suffered; or a guilty woman who acted maliciously. The truth may be some combination of the three, but each possibility presents its own ethical complications. As far as I can calculate, Lafarge and I have the same sun and moon sign (Capricorn and Leo, respectively), so I like to tell myself that helps with her voice.

Who are some of your favorite poets?

As an early reader, Sylvia Plath, Mina Loy, and Rita Dove. Stevie Nicks and the Dixie Chicks. In college, my friend and professor Kazim Ali introduced me to *Nightboat Books* and its many wonderful poets: Michael Burkard, Bhanu Kapil, and Brandon Som.

If you had to narrow it down, what three books have had the most impact on your writing?

Thomas and Beulah by Rita Dove; *Tsim Tsum* by Sabrina Orah Mark; *The Vertical Interrogation of Strangers* by Bhanu Kapil.

Based on your personal experience, what advice would you give to other writers?

More observation than advice, but I've noticed the more I practice the daily rituals that are good for my body and spirit in general—meditation, gardening, jogging, flossing—the more patience and creativity I have with my craft and the better I navigate some of the more negative aspects of the publishing world, like jealousy and self-doubt.

What is the best piece of writing advice you've been given?

Malena Mörling once told my graduate poetry workshop to always ask of a poem: "Where is the light?" She meant this literally—from what vantage point are your images illuminated? This might be part of why I'm often preoccupied with gems and jewels in my work. I use them as symbols for ancestry and heirlooms, but they also hold light. I've read people are drawn to the gloss and shine of jewels because their reflections mimic sunlight on clean water, that this attraction stems from the biological impulse for thirst. I find this beautiful. Formatting a poem on the page also reminds me of jewelry as well. I imagine myself as a lapidary. Each line break or indentation is a freshly cut facet that better helps an image hold its light.

Where can readers find more of your work?

My forthcoming chapbook *Hypochondria, Least Powerful of the Greek Gods* is available for pre-order with *Glass Poetry Press*. I'm very excited for this project. I anthropomorphized my health anxiety into the character of a Greek goddess. She dates Poseidon and is terrified of mirrors.

Readers can also visit my website (emilypaigewilson.com) for selected poems.

DISASSOCIATION
KAY LIN

NEWSPAPER: Student on Financial Assistance Takes Top Score.
PHOTOGRAPH: one-room flat, stacked garbage, uniformed
boy in centre, sores covering his hands. books lie haphazard
on the floor, pages yellowed and scattered, bindings ripped.
ARTICLE: rubbish collector father, diabetic mother, balancing
schoolwork with roadside sales of tissue papers. a clear inspiration.

MEMORY: flat with three bedrooms, an empty
savings account. wooden shelves of
different shades, folded clothes and
boxes at the top, plastic-sealed books
piled at the bottom. a girl seated at the
table, textbook for then-new syllabus
held loose one hand, the other thumbing
edges of mah-jong tiles. cigarette smoke,
gamblers' rough tenors ring laughter.

LITERATURE: Unemployed Man Accidentally Kills Daughter.
ILLUSTRATION: ratty singlet, unshaven chin, guilt like dirt
clinging to hairy arms. behind him, four children huddle
beneath a table where a half-eaten packet of noodles lie.
SYPNOSIS: drunkard father, disabled child, helpless mother.
a moment of rash anger ending in a tombstone.

MEMORY: beer bottle sweating condensation,
forgotten for classifieds in three
languages. candles burn, daughter at
makeshift stove, long burns up and
down her unlearned arms. father's
chopsticks tremble, overladen with
an abundance of half-spoiled meat on
way to daughter's bowl. mother returns
at midnight, sleeps only four hours.

MAGAZINE: Teacher Helps Valedictorian Overcome Adversity.
PHOTOGRAPH: university auditorium, young woman in rented
graduation gown, parents bracketing. camera flashes highlight
heavy wrinkles, obscures pride. a man in a suit stands centre.
ARTICLE: parents are menial labourers, no education to help
daughter. young teacher, full of passion, gives encouragement.

MEMORY: new office, new desk, new graduate.
blazer frayed at the cuffs. text message
sent to once-teacher in thanks for loan,
mind calculating total cost of debts owed.
ceremony skipped for work. first paycheque
stretches longer without rental fees to pay:
new heater, new windows, new dentures
for mother. picture taken wearing t-shirt
at fancy restaurant in three-star hotel.

INTERVIEW

WITH KAY LIN

What inspired the poem?

The poem was very much inspired by my own personal experiences and how they contrasted with the way poverty has been and still is represented in Singapore. I grew up along—and, at times, barely above—the poverty line in Singapore, and nothing in any form of media, whether in the news or magazines or even fiction, captures my lived experiences. The title, "disassociation," summarises exactly how I feel when I have to read and/or study those pieces of media in school, and then returning home to the reality of poverty, which is far more complex.

Part of the poem was inspired by my anger. Representations of poverty in the past had always been talking about physically abusive and drunk fathers, cowering mothers, filthy living conditions, and—something unique to Singapore—broken or non-existent English ability. It's better nowadays, but many of the representations of poverty are still from the flawed perspectives of those who are middle or higher in terms of socioeconomic class. "disassociation" is my attempt to write about poverty from the perspective of someone who has actually grown up within its environment.

How much revision went into this poem? / How long do you usually spend working on a single poem?

There were five drafts; this is the fifth. Every 'draft' was a complete rewrite from the first word to the last. My first draft was written in October 2015, and the fifth draft was written in November 2018. That's approximately one draft every ten months or so.

I don't spend time writing a single poem exactly. My process tends to be writing a whole bunch of them at once, putting them away for a few months, and then attacking them again once I've completely forgotten what I've written. Part of this is because my day job keeps me extremely busy, but another part of it is my personal philosophy: if I can't tell what the point of the poem is after leaving it alone for a few months, then no reader will be able to tell, which means I need to revamp the poem entirely. Whether the rewrite is to clarify the main idea behind the poem or to change its primary theme entirely depends on the poem I'm working on.

Was there anything in your original conception that did not make it in?

The previous drafts had a lot more detail about my personal experiences and quite a bit more ranting about the newspaper and magazine articles. I cut it all out because it was unnecessary.

Is this poem categorical of your work? Why or why not?

Thematically, yes, this poem is very much categorical of my work; many of my poems focus on the various, supposedly mundane aspects of poverty as a lived experience. However, "disassociation" is one of the most "culture-less" of my poems: the others in the chapbook I have recently finished touched a great deal on my culture as an overseas Chinese person who has been brought up in a very traditional home.

Who are some of your favorite poets?

Margaret Atwood, for her use of perspective. Seamus Heaney, for his use of realism and language. Kate Tempest, for her sense of rhythm and beautiful way of capturing the mundanity of experiences. Carol Ann Duffy, for her insistence on simplicity and accessibility. Chinaka Hodge, for her sense of rhythm and raw honesty of language. Boey Kim Cheng, for showing me that Singapore can be written in a way that isn't political or confessional, but instead revealing truths about the country in a way that is raw, personal, and with genuine heart.

Based on your personal experience, what advice would you give to other writers?

"Just because it doesn't work right now doesn't mean it won't work later." Some of my poems took five years and over ten drafts before they reach a stage that I'm happy with, and I had wanted to give up on them and throw them into the trash at points, but I didn't, and now I have an entire chapbook full of poems that I'm proud to put to print with my name on it.

What is the best piece of writing advice you've been given?

One of the best pieces of writing advice I was given is: "everything must have a purpose." I find it especially true for poetry, in which the form creates the first impression, the language is condensed, and every image must overlay and work with each other. I worked hard to ensure that everything can create a single message even as I made sure that there are other potential interpretations embedded in the text as well as subtleties in meaning for those who would take the time to give it a closer look.

I'm cheating a little, but I must state the *other* best piece of advice, which I find just as important as the above: "make it accessible." This is incredibly important to me because I write about poverty; if I write in a manner that's overly complicated and requires a literary education to understand the story and message, then it will be hypocritical to the message itself as I'll be cutting out the very people that the poem is about.

Where can readers find more of your work?

My chapbook, *symptoms of the forgotten*, won the 2019 Open Country Press Chapbook Contest. It includes "disassociation" and fourteen other poems, and will be published by *Open Country* in 2020. Please look out for it!

GAIA

CHELSEA JACKSON

Eyes Aurora Borealis green, she inspects
her spoiling breasts in the bathroom mirror
ice caps seeping into the bile of her chest
where nothing but heartbeat survives
where floating fish pulse.

She spits into the sink, pauses
to watch the foam of her curdled oceans
orbit the rubber sun of the drain.
Infection that will soon make its way back inside her
for nothing truly leaves, everything mutates.   Somewhere,

which is to say, everywhere,
at this moment, which is to say
always, she sweeps aside the branches
of her *Eupherbia mili* hair, to trace
the handprints seared into her neck

and reaches between bruised thighs, to lift hands
bathed in blood. Bitter she laughs,
vomits cement onto her reflection.
Finger-paints 'Pangea.'
                    As vitriolic men return to her battered door

to harvest her lungs
paint her forests USD green
suck marrow from her bones
take pliers to her toe nails and eye lashes
for good measure.

INTERVIEW
WITH CHELSEA JACKSON

What inspired the poem?

I wrote this piece in the fall of 2018. It grew from the frustration and disgust I felt regarding our society's treatment of the earth. I also am inspired by mythology of all kinds and decided to write about the Greek goddess Gaia.

What was the hardest part about writing it?

One of the hardest things about writing this piece was the heaviness of the content—its association with assault and abuse. From a craft standpoint, I wanted to make sure to balance the listing and expansion of images, so there are some images that move quickly, and others I spend more time with. However, they all revolve around this central image of Gaia wounded in a bathroom.

Was there anything in your original conception that did not make it in?

In the very beginning, the piece was built around the image of painting trees "USD green." I was struck by the irony of cutting down green forests, to make green paper that only has value because we give it power. In that early draft I broke that forest image open and described the animals of the forest as witnesses of this destruction. However, as the piece evolved, and I brought in the character of Gaia, the animals no longer fit.

Is this poem categorical of your work? Why or why not?

This piece is pretty categorical of my work. I love to write with strong images and create multi-layered poetry that speaks to individual and societal concerns.

What is your favorite line from the poem or the line you are most proud of?

One that sticks out is the one I added in the most recent revision, "…she sweeps aside the branches / of her *Eupherbia mili* hair, to trace / the handprints seared into her neck"

I especially love the *Eupherbia mili*, because if a reader wants to take the extra step of looking up that plant, they will find its nickname is the "Crown of Thorns" or the "Christ Plant." Therefore, it's a bit of embedded invitation for the reader to consider what is deemed holy/sacred. Who gets to make that choice? How do we treat, talk about, or remember those things (or people) that are deemed holy and those that are not?

Is there anything unique about your personal writing process?

My process has changed over time. More recently, I will have an image or line pop into my mind, but I can tell the full poem isn't ready to be written yet. I have several pages in my notebook that are just these fragments of images and lines. Then usually, if it sits on the back burner of my mind long enough, something will happen. Maybe I'll get another line, or I'll feel ready and excited to explore the image, then I'll know it's time to sit down and write the piece.

Other times my process is more straightforward. I'll sit down with a general idea or prompt and physically write the whole piece in one sitting. Right after writing it, I'll transfer it to the computer and do a quick revision. Then I'll leave it for a while, and when I come back, maybe a week or maybe three months later, I will usually hone the piece even more. Over time, I'll keep honing, until I have the urge to share it with someone other than my partner or my dog.

How long have you been writing poetry? What has changed from your first poem to your newest work?

I've been writing poetry since I was about fourteen, but I didn't really start sharing my work until about ten years later in graduate school, when I found a writing community that supported me (shout-out to ARTS by the People in Morristown, New Jersey!). Since I began writing more seriously and working with other poets and mentors, my overall understanding of, and relationship to, poetry has evolved. My writing has become less apologetic and more direct, and I'm more confident in experimenting with different forms. I've also gained a greater respect for the relationship between the poet and the reader. There is agency and empowerment in both the writing of poetry, and the reading of it. Each poem I write is an invitation for readers to go as shallow or as deep as they want. The place where that invitation is extended by the poet and accepted by the reader is a really magical space.

If you had to narrow it down, what three books have had the most impact on your writing?

Though there are many, I'd say the following three books have really helped shape my writing: Patricia Smith's *Blood Dazzler* is amazing and really opened my eyes to the use of frame, personification, and storytelling to write poems that speak to significant events and injustices; Douglas Kearney's *Patter* empowered me to write about hard topics and not be afraid to experiment with a poem's form and shape; Judy Grahn's *The Work of A Common Woman* demonstrates a wide range of voice. Her long poem "A Woman is Talking to Death" is haunting, and has motivated me to try writing my own long poem, which is tricky.

Based on your personal experience, what advice would you give to other writers?

Revise with courage. Sometimes I think we can hold on to words, lines, and images the poem wants to shed, but revision means we are getting closer to what the piece wants to say. Plus, cutting lines and images just means you have more material for another poem.

What is the best piece of writing advice you've been given?

Trust your reader, and write with enough clarity (and confidence) that you don't feel the need to summarize or provide exposition at the end of all your poems.

Also, the personal is political; the individual, universal. This piece of advice made my writing so much stronger because it allowed me to explore big, abstract ideas and issues in a more concentrated and consumable way.

Where can readers find more of your work?

I am currently making final edits on my first poetry manuscript and will soon be sending it out to publishers. Fingers crossed! In the meantime, folks can find me at Twitter and Instagram (@sea_c_j).

After Aiden Dies Halfway Through Chemo

JANIRU LIYANAGE

his bones, irradiated to thick
yellow lines of fat
I peel and peel and cannot
come apart
it's winter now and we never
drank enough milk or ate enough
meat and I never spooned
you enough pills
I say a prayer over my
body and sink into the scent
of lilacs and hoarfrost
then, outside, everything
wilding around me - glut of
bones so soft, you could melt them
with your palms
I run a blade under my skin and cleave
out a blossom   an entire saint
outside, a boy gathers up baseballs,
unstitches horse leather, and unfurls it
to the bone

INTERVIEW
WITH JANIRU LIYANGE

What inspired the poem?

This poem came after my mother's aunt passed away, who died from breast cancer. I distinctly remember seeing her when we went back to Sri Lanka, just before she died. Her face was almost limned; angelic and radiant. It was, so beautiful for a moment, the whole world around us, quietening. That was a few years ago. After only recently finding poetry as a means to divert the quiet rumble in my head, I remembered this memory and just wrote.

What was the hardest part about writing it?

So much of my family hates talking about events like this. Grief is such an imbued but painful memory in my family and we don't talk about it, for both personal and superstitious reasons. So I grew up in a home internalising the idea that I shouldn't talk about such things and so to write this poem, to open up a wound in my family's past and to be vulnerable like this was difficult. Another part of this vulnerability was to be honest enough to honour my grand-aunt and my own grief. I've been writing a series of poems titled with the persona "Aiden," who's a stand-in as a personification of my grief overall, and so not having to mention my great aunt by name or relation to me was easier for me and my family to handle.

How much revision went into this poem?

I wrote the poem in one sitting, pretty much in the exact form it is now—it was truly an outpour of grief. But I know this poem wasn't just sudden and spontaneous or rash. Rather, this poem has been with me for years. I've been carrying it, turning it over in my mind, chipping away at the scene of seeing my grand-aunt, dying and sickly on her bed but shimmering in the roiling half-light coming in from above her.

Is this poem categorical of your work? Why or why not?

Most of my poems revolve around the oppression of my people: the civil war and colonisation. The essence of my poetry is to pass a mic and give a voice to the ghosts haunting my people: to the griefs my family refuses to speak about. So in a way, it is slightly categorical of my work, being to a ghost of mine. But in another, the context of her "ghost-hood", as I like to call it, is not in the same vein as the much of my other work.

How long do you usually spend working on a single poem?

It depends on how ready I am to write the poem. Sometimes, a poem can go through various drafts, each in different forms. For instance, I'll sometimes take a poem in couplets or several lines and remove all or most of its punctuation and make it prose just to see it in a different light. Those poems usually meditate with me for up to weeks and are almost never in their final forms even after sending them out to journals and magazines. Other times, a poem, like this one, would've already spun itself to life in my head. In these rare occasions, poetry becomes a way to let the essence of that poem bring itself into the world. These poems are often written in one sitting or so.

How long have you been writing poetry? What has changed from your first poem to your newest work?

I've been writing for pretty much a year now. Compared to my earlier works, I've learnt a lot more about form, about being succinct and not ruining the language of poetry by idling and rambling on and on about ideas. I've learnt to cut to the point but not answer all my questions, because sometimes I just won't have an answer—in those cases, I've learnt that the poem is in fact better. I've learnt about the necessity of a volta or several voltas in a poem, having it go multiple directions and giving it space to grow in different dimensions.

Who are some of your favorite poets?

My favourites are Kaveh Akbar, Paige Lewis, Ocean Vuong, Danez Smith, Franny Choi, Jane Wong, Fatimah Asghar, Cameron Awkward Rich, Ruth Awad, and a whole host of others. (You should really check them all out!)

If you had to narrow it down, what three books have had the most impact on your writing?

That's tough—every book I've read has shaped my voice, which is still changing. But the books that have been behind my biggest steps would have to be *Calling a Wolf a Wolf* by Kaveh Akbar, *The January Children* by Safia Elhillo, and *Gamperaliya* by Martin Wickramasinghe, a Sri Lankan writer who, though long dead, was the first one to teach me how literature can be a powerful way to help be a voice for your quietened people.

What is the best piece of writing advice you've been given?

This wasn't given personally to me (but I think everything I come across is something for me to learn from) but Danez Smith, while discussing on a podcast, talked about how important it is to become a student of form. Learning poetic form and becoming a student of it has really changed my approach to poetry altogether. Sometimes, form itself will carry me through when the original mess in my head wouldn't have.

Where can readers find more of your work?

Right now, some of my most recent online poems appear or are forthcoming in places such as *[PANK]*, *Wildness, Homology Lit, Ekphrastic Review, Cordite Poetry Review* and elsewhere. For more, see my website (janiruliyanage.weebly.com).

LAWN BODIES

JOHN DAVIS JR.

Dwight called me *dumpster bastard*
with too much truth in his voice.

So I struck him hard in the jaw
and he fell, hitting his blond head
on our front-yard rain tree's trunk.

                    He didn't get up. I ran.

My stepfather, preparing to mow,
found Dwight coldcocked minutes later,
and fireman-carried him
to his grandparents next door.

                    Boys...What can you do?

After icing the headache,
Dwight came back, invited me to the dirt
hole he'd dug behind his Pa-paw's shop.
Red plastic ninjas and dollar-store commandos

filled fingernail-crafted caves in its walls.
Soon, they would drown in a garden-hose flood,
lose ground to die-cast cars and trucks
until we filled the void with leveled soil.

                    Another year, and we wouldn't cross the fence.

The rain tree sheds its yellow blooms,
and they are breeze-rolled over our older lawns
before settling, dispersed or crushed on the road.

INTERVIEW
WITH JOHN DAVID JR.

What inspired the poem?

This piece is semi-autobiographical. I really did have a fist fight with a neighbor kid (his name wasn't Dwight), and he really did get knocked out cold by a tree behind him. The rest is a hodgepodge of poignant recollections from my friendship with this boy.

What came easiest when writing this poem?

Memories from childhood always seem to come easy because when you're small, you tend to remember everything in vivid, colorful detail. Those memories remain pretty sharp over the years and wind their way into my work little by little.

How much revision went into this poem?

All my poems tend to go through about five drafts before they enter the "fine touches" stage. This one went through significantly more because it evolved over a couple of years. Among other things, its shape kept changing.

Is this poem categorical of your work? Why or why not?

This poem is pretty standard for me. I like writing about old neighborhoods, the friends and foes there, and the lessons learned from them. I tend to gravitate toward rural subjects usually, and while this piece is a little more suburban, it still smacks of country experience, I believe.

What is your favorite line from the poem or the line you are most proud of?

"Red plastic ninjas and dollar-store commandos" is probably the line I like the most, just because I can see those figurines in my head so clearly, and I'm sure readers can, too. I'm a fan of the concrete image.

How long do you usually spend working on a single poem?

It varies. Some poems get a week's worth of attention before I put them away to revise later, while other poems may hang around for months or even years before I feel they're truly ready to be revisited.

How long have you been writing poetry? What has changed from your first poem to your newest work?

I've been writing what I'd call "real" poetry for about twenty years now. My first poems were terribly overburdened with alliteration and cheap, gimmicky tricks of language (puns, meaningless internal rhymes, etc.), and while I still have to watch my propensity to fall back on those, I tend to cull them now more than I would have as a young poet.

If you had to narrow it down, what three books have had the most impact on your writing?

The Triggering Town by Richard Hugo for its practicality and forthright style; *To Kill a Mockingbird* by Harper Lee for its rich portrayal of small-town life and the people that make it; and *The Poetry Home Repair Manual* by Ted Kooser for its earthy, plainspoken guide to literary life.

BLENDER

WREN TUATHA

Something needs to be said.
Who can hear it over the threats
of a Sunday night blender?
Vegan cream of broccoli.
Cashews do the job.
I stare like a cow, thinking
of an old West Wing episode.

I have wasted my life. Minutes
rip through the projector, sliced
once they're seen. I have regrets.

There's a surgical tool,
a morcellator, that rips
sections of my womb
like a Hollywood alien,
like muscular hands twisting
a poor clementine, removable
through a contained incision.

Humans want credit for minutes
of kindness, The Sistine Chapel
and Woodstock, while doing
nothing to unplug morcellators.

A blender, a history book.
Inhaled melancholy of my blank stare.

INTERVIEW

WITH WREN TUATHA

What inspired the poem?

A friend in an online poetry group posted a question of ennui. Something poetically phrased, along the lines of, "what's the point of it all?" I firmly believe we're on our own, no dad on a cloud. So it's our opportunity to make meaning. Yet I'm often disappointed that we humans get in our own way, settle for mediocre, until the whole thing is such a mess no one knows where to start, so we don't. This seems true, individually and collectively.

From left field—I had my uterus removed after decades of being very ill with uterine fibroids. The surgeon wanted to use this morcellator tool, which is just as messy as it sounds. If the patient has cancer there, the mocellator tosses it throughout the area and it spreads. Patient survival rates after that are about zero. The FDA issued a warning for surgeons to not use this tool. That it is still used is symptomatic of our inertia.

How much revision went into this poem?

Like most of my poems, I got my ideas down in a first draft. Then I revised and put away; revised and put away. I can say I revised it right up to publication, because Jerrod had some great suggestions, which I accepted. As an editor myself, I know it's dicey to suggest edits to a poem. But I was happy to have him point out what I couldn't see.

How long do you usually spend working on a single poem?

I have poems I've been revising for years. I would say my average is probably three to six months.

How long have you been writing poetry? What has changed from your first poem to your newest work?

I've been poeming since I learned to spell words like grass and sky. My process is evolving now that I'm in Goddard's MFA program. I always read poetry. But reading books with and eye toward annotating some point of craft has deepened my inner dialog of what a poem can do and how my work does or does not achieve its goals. Suddenly, I pull poems of my own out of reading others. It's new for me to have a daily writing practice with no goal assumed. That's been fruitful. I think the biggest change from my first poem about grass and sky to now, is that I've learned to modulate my ego more appropriately. It's so easy to write something and think it's amazing and be indignant or deflated when others don't agree. I've learned to seek others' impressions, detach from the outcome, and keep revising!

Who are some of your favorite poets?

Eileen Myles, Jericho Brown, Camille T. Dungy, Joy Harjo, Adrienne Rich, Natalie Diaz, Robert Duncan, Marge Piercy, Minnie Bruce Pratt, Allison Joseph, Molly Fisk, and C.T. when he dances…

Based on your personal experience, what advice would you give to other writers?

Find the advice that fits your goals. The best thing I have done for my writing is my MFA. Not everyone can access that path or invest the time. There are many paths. Find ways to actually challenge yourself, find a writing community. Question your assumptions and investigate. Revise. Read. Sit in a field of goats, but don't bring paper with you.

Where can readers find more of your work?

I have a collection, *Thistle and Brilliant*, at *Finishing Line Press*. And many of my published poems are online. I'm included in *California Fire & Water, A Climate Crisis Anthology*, edited by Molly Fisk.

AMERICA BABY

TURANDOT SHAYEGAN

baby, i am arch&dirt town. i am town town. this body for worship, eatup. baby, i wanna be you. i wanna unpeal my mangofleshhot and charred i wanna eat myself in Honey Barbecue i wanna manifestmanifestManifest. baby, i wanna be you. bigBaby. i wanna sell flesh onflesh onflesh and find out it's Mine. hot and cold stockroom pounds of Me i wanna shovel it downDown. i wanna scrubthebloodbackintomyskin. baby, i wanna be you. i wanna snort genocide&gerrymander ovaries. so many fucking ovaries, i wanna make&break whores. baby, i wanna be you. baby, baby, i wanna be You&god. whositwhatsit to you? baby, Big baby, Sweet baby, Soft baby. Blood baby, America baby, my baby.

INTERVIEW
WITH TURANDOT SHAYEGAN

What inspired the poem?

"America Baby" is a poem about idolization, reverence, and blind worship. It is meant to reflect our deep-rooted patriotism—a patriotism blind to America's legacy of bloodshed and violence. This is a brutal love. To deny America her history is to mutilate her, and to love the patchwork history is to love that mutilation. I wrote "America Baby" to confront our longing for this half-America. It reflects a deification, a desperate craving for American smoothness, for peaceful suburbia, for conveyor and plastic, for carbohydrate, for the American dream. It is a love so unconditional that this dream is not to be American, but to become America, to unzip the national skin and meld into bone and beating heart. I wrote "America Baby" because it is the heart and the beating. Past and present, America beats and then buries unmarked. I am marking.

What was the hardest part about writing it?

Even ironically, mockingly, it was difficult to write from a perspective of adoration and devotion. It was difficult to express love for what is a broken and vicious system. I hope that by doing so, the contrast between love and violence reveals the perversion in our love and how deeply we are committed to this perversion.

What came easiest when writing this poem?

I found it easiest to explore the meaning of the word "baby." I used "baby" as a seductive term, a sensual flirtation with the Americana, an almost erotic fascination with our country. I also used the word "baby" to reflect our raw, childlike relationship with America, our unrefined and infantile simplicity.

Is this poem categorical of your work? Why or why not?

My writing is always inspired by the world around me, focusing especially on inequality and bodily autonomy. Although all of my poems are not about American identity, they draw greatly on American life. Overwhelmingly, I focus on language and the appearance and sound of a word. I fall in love with the way words break together, the way they hold one another, the way they whisper. I fall in love with words that spit and pray and taste, words that eat and live. I think words are brutal and fleshy and raw. I think words are barbaric. I think words are beautiful.

Is there anything unique about your personal writing process?

I think my poems are very emotionally charged. I allow myself to feel angry, to feel sad, to taste and touch every word that I write. I try to live my poems and breathe my poems. I write until I have become every letter, every curve, ever spike, every cavity. I write until the poem has been wholly transfixed into me and I into it—until we are a bloodline.

What has changed from your first poem to your newest work?

From my first poem to my newest work, I have developed my relationship with language. I have experimented with spacing—large gaps, broken lines, or no spaces at all—in order to slow or increase the pace of the poem. I have experimented with all capital letters and all lowercase letters, with unconventional punctuation and grammar, with verse and prose poetry. I have come to understand that language is crucial to poetry, and crucial to our experience as readers.

How would you personally define poetry?

Poetry is a mother, a maker, a child. Poetry is a misdemeanor. Poetry is to dissect and dissociate, is cold water that clings from your neck, is bits of flesh uncurled from the fennel. Poetry is reverse-baptist, in debt and uprooted. Poetry is behind on rent, is the shuck and the liver, is the crate and the underneath. Poetry is the cadaver. Poetry is un-heavenly and sometimes a body. Poetry is to unpeel and corrupt. Poetry is survival, salvation.

BRUISES FROM GOD

JOANNA LEE

blurred margins divide the darkness, headed west.
smell of anti-ocean, of home, of hope embered out—
cigarette burn in the aquamarine nap of a border town hotel room
where a short-skirted missionary drips
candlewax on the cockroaches
and would-be angels play the same records, killing
time in the same skipped grooves. turns
out those bird cries were never from real birds.
turns out you would've been a great mother:
all those nights in the methadone ward, walking,
singing some old stolen lament
from somewhere you'll never see. all those songs
you keep still tucked like pocket aces, like the cracked quena
in the crawlspace that belonged to the first
wild-eyed boy to crack your heart.
it wasn't the same, after—not the redbuds,
not the spring. rolling the guilt round your tongue,
you never did learn to whistle.
there. there. put heat on it. it encourages the blood
to return.

INTERVIEW

What inspired the poem?

Driving along interstate 64 east, the road that goes from Richmond to the ocean. In the spring, the new yellow-greens and the blooming of the redbuds along the highway make it a blur of yellows and purples...like a fading bruise.

What was the hardest part about writing it?

Once I started writing, the initial memory triggered several other memory-images in succession. Figuring out which ones belonged and how they connected to build the arc of the poem was the most challenging part.

What came easiest when writing this poem?

Surprisingly, the title! Titles are generally hard for me, but this one was very nearly a starting point.

Was there anything in your original conception that did not make it in?

There were images/references both to sainthood and to whiskey in earlier versions—neither made it in this final cut!

How much revision went into this poem?

About an average amount? I've read it aloud several times at readings or open mics, and it would get a tweak before or after each. Then a separate round of edits—hard copy, red pen, and all—before sending it out into the world on submission.

Is this poem categorical of your work? Why or why not?

Yes, in that it is image-based and melancholy and has both natural and medical references. Which I guess is about as particularly characteristic of my writing as you can get.

How long have you been writing poetry? What has changed from your first poem to your newest work?

Since I was six or seven...? I like to think my work's gotten better since then.

Who are some of your favorite poets?

Currently crushing on Ocean Vuong and Kaveh Akbar. Love Rafael Campo, too. Claudia Emerson. Kim Addonizio. More classically, Walt Whitman, Sylvia Plath, and Anne Sexton; also Pablo Neruda and Federico Garcia Lorca.

Based on your personal experience, what advice would you give to other writers?

(1) There's no substitution for putting your butt in the chair and writing. (2) Always read your work aloud as part of your editing process. (3) Never think a piece is above editing.

LANDMINE

KATHERINE FALLON

Pastures gone dun and twinkling with frost,
there is new work for you to do. The cattle
have all been slaughtered, and the chickens

put themselves away at night. First, attach
a hose to the farm truck tailpipe. Watch
your breath fuse with fumes or winter. Now,

shove the thing deep into the tunnels,
which are the prairie dogs' doing. You are
to thread the hose into the burrows until

it hits a barrier too tight for passage and let it
clean house, a softer ending than some.
Between rounds, forget it. Rest knowing

the cows that broke bones in the minefield
went lame, got lean, and so were made
to take sooner bullets than they should.

INTERVIEW

WITH KATHERINE FALLON

What inspired the poem?

I worked for a few seasons on a grass-fed cattle ranch in Colorado. I wasn't squeamish about death before then, but it also hadn't been my job to kill anything yet. There were many lessons like this one while working there, and I have written about a number of them before, but the prairie dogs were a collateral concern and I wanted to give them space.

What was the hardest part about writing it?

Creating a second-person directive: do this, do this, do this. I had recently given myself a note to write this way more often, as the pieces I have written this way have been successful. I tend to get mired in the first-person, so it did prove challenging, especially in this context of giving myself awful marching orders.

How much revision went into this poem?

A lot. Primarily in rearranging and considering word choice in an effort to diminish the effects of ego and sentimentality.

Is this poem categorical of your work? Why or why not?

Thematically, yes, but stylistically, no. I write a lot about working on the farm, and about the hand I had in killing things, and, well, about death in general, but the tone of the poem is novel to me.

What is your favorite line from the poem or the line you are most proud of?

The final stanza is my favorite. I often know an ending when I start a poem, but that wasn't the case here. It all unfolded line-by-line, and that final bit gave me a lot of trouble: what is the takeaway in a story like this one? I am happy with where it landed, in that liminal space between guilt and detachment.

Who are some of your favorite poets?

Adrienne Rich, Gabrielle Calvocoressi, Mark Doty, Jean Valentine, Anne Carson, Li-Young Lee, Nicole Steinberg, Emma Bolden, Maya Pindyck, and Maggie Nelson.

Do you work in any other artistic mediums? If so, how do those other genres inform your poetry?

I dabble in fiction. It is difficult for me to understand how verbose I am in prose (my short stories are often too long for submission guidelines), and how spare in my poems, and I oftentimes get confused about which genre best suits an idea. I also make miniatures from clay, which sometimes requires a literal magnifying glass. That definitely assists me in winnowing words, as well as deciding how much detail is too much detail for something so tiny and self-contained.

What is the best piece of writing advice you've been given?

Read other writers, and talk to them if they'll have you.

Where can readers find more of your work?

Upcoming in *AGNI, Natural Bridge, Into the Void,* and *Levee*. Recently in *Best New Poets 2019, Minola Review, COUNTERCLOCK,* and *Normal School*. I have a chapbook, *The Toothmakers' Daughters,* through *Finishing Line Press,* and my first full-length collection, *Bridle,* is forthcoming through *Eyewear Publishing, Ltd.* Readers can visit my website for past publications (www.katherinefallon.com).

What drew you to *Driftwood Press*?

Aside from enjoying your content and design, I was attracted to your relationship with your writers. It is not often one is offered an opportunity to engage in an interview such as this one at the relative start of one's career. Acceptance is certainly a victory; conversation is infinitely humanizing.

THE LIGHTNING BOX ON THE EDGE OF BOYKIN CREEK

MADELEINE FRANK

There is a lightning box that sits on the edge of Boykin Creek. Two boys are missing their high school basketball game to fuss around with the lock.

Do y'all hear that?

The mud slipping down the banks and the cicadas crackling on the far shore? The box is slick with light, the boys' fingers rusting from the corners. The box is burning off the tips of their fingernails, trapping light in the beds. It's somehow cemented to the ground through roots and grime and spider's silk. Maybe the box is filled with worms, no, caterpillars, no wait, butterflies. But no, they'd all be dead.

Dead. Dead. Dead.

The light would've scorched them, burnt them to a crisp, it's so goddamn bright (they can't see it, but they know). One of the boys is fixing to go back to the truck. He says it won't start if he leaves it still too long. The other one jams a twig he snapped from a magnolia into the keyhole of the box. His knees are crunching beetle shells and creek water is lapping at his ankles. The sun is setting over some ledge as the boys clamor on all fours up the cut, wincing as the light exits their fingers.

INTERVIEW

WITH MADELEINE FRANK

What was the hardest part about writing it?

I had to decide how much explaining to do. Too much and it would become micro-fiction. Too little and it would be completely nonsensical (and not in a good, poetry-type way).

What came easiest when writing this poem?

I knew at the very start of writing this poem what I wanted the setting to be—southern, secluded, and natural. From there, it was relatively easy (or perhaps "enjoyable" is a better word) to build up imagery in that space.

How much revision went into this poem?

The largest revision was to the structure. Originally, it was just a wall of text. Then, Sarah Barber, a wonderful poet and professor, pointed out that it needed to be broken up. In the end, I chose to separate out the lines that were breaking up the rhythm of the poem anyway—one that speaks directly to someone and one with repetition.

Is this poem categorical of your work? Why or why not?

Yes, in that it's focused around bizarre or unexplainable imagery. In this case, it's the "lightning box," a fictional object. I am also partial to narratives in my poetry, whatever form they may come in.

What is your favorite line from the poem or the line you are most proud of?

"Two boys are missing their high school basketball game to fuss around with the lock." I think that I managed to pack a lot of background into that line without having to write everything out separately.

How long do you usually spend working on a single poem?

Usually, I'll have one line that I know I want to include in a poem written down somewhere for a while before I actually figure out how to write the whole piece. In this case, the line was, "There is a lightning box that sits on the edge of Boykin Creek." Then, I write the poem within a few hours.

Editing and revision usually take me a few months, not because I'm changing that much, but because I often become preoccupied with new lines for new poems.

Do you work in any other artistic mediums? If so, how do those other genres inform your poetry?

My main genre is actually creative nonfiction. I write a lot of humor memoir about my experience in my body and in the world around me. Often, I'll write a poem and an essay about the same moment, feeling, or place. I find that poetry helps me explore emotion and imagery more freely, while nonfiction helps me be precise and clear in my language. Because of this, lines from poems often show up in my essays, and scenes from these essays often turn into poems.

Based on your personal experience, what advice would you give to other writers?

Forget about what poem (or essay, or story) you think you're "supposed" to write. For a while, I was cranking out love poems with metaphors about religion all written in the most flowery language I could manage. When I gave up on that and started actually writing about things that were interesting to me (and in ways that were interesting to me), my work improved and my poetic voice became clearer.

Where can readers find more of your work?

I recently published a poem in *Sheila-Na-Gig* online. I also have a TEDx talk, "The Art of Shit-Talking," that's available to watch on YouTube.

THE PORT BEGAT THE STORM

MOLLY OBERSTEIN-ALLEN

Leaning out the window of a smoldering lighthouse, sowing raindrops from the sea.

Radio: *A water droplet weighs 50 times as much as a mosquito.*

The ring at the bottom of my coffee cup announces the imminence of death.
We've been in this room for so long. Dust piles under the door, dust outlines our bodies.

Radio: *A mosquito, hit by a water droplet, is absorbed by it rather than being crushed.*
Encased in the water droplet, it tumbles down.
If it doesn't free itself before the ground comes rushing—

Static.

The floor is growing warm. How big is this place? Did we ever have a chance here?
The safe house consumed us in the end, I guess.

Small comfort that the dust too will burn
Small comfort that worse things have happened
Small comfort, the water and the air and the sea

INTERVIEW

WITH MOLLY OBERSTEIN-ALLEN

How much revision went into this poem?

I wrote two drafts of this poem and then I took it to a writer's circle that I used to be part of. The wonderful writers there helped me hone the poem immensely—they helped me figure out what it was about and communicate that more clearly. After meeting with them I changed the poem around a lot and then kept tweaking it until it felt right.

I will say that having a writing circle is amazing—it encourages me to keep working on projects I might otherwise just give up on or call complete before they're ready, and it helps me practice giving and accepting criticism more gracefully and constructively. I'd encourage anyone to join a writing group if they're trying to improve their writing or just get into a more regular writing practice.

How long have you been writing poetry? What has changed from your first poem to your newest work?

I've been writing poetry for as long as I can remember, in fits and spurts.

When I was in middle school I was institutionalized for awhile and I would write all these really long, myopic, depressing poems. I'd write poetry pretty much every day and show my writing to this one staffer whom I really connected with. Her seeing and validating my shitty poems made such a huge difference to me. It inspired me to keep writing and sharing vulnerable parts of myself. If you're reading this, Miss Dana, thank you forever.

My poetry now is a lot less navel-gazey—I'd like to think that it's more lyrical and more mature than it used to be.

Who are some of your favorite poets?

Ilya Kaminsky, Dalton Day, Joshua Jennifer Espinoza, Morgan Parker, Dorothea Lasky. Yeats. Nana Grizol.

If you had to narrow it down, what three books have had the most impact on your writing?

Priestdaddy by Patricia Lockwood. That book is seriously laugh-out-loud funny and just so raw. I felt like I was at summer camp trying to stop giggling in my sleeping bag the whole time I was reading it. And I love that it takes place largely in Kansas City, where I live!

On Earth We're Briefly Gorgeous by Ocean Vuong. I think it's worth mentioning that both this and Priestdaddy are novels by poets—they create these really lyrical, rich narratives that feel so natural and personal.

How Should A Person Be by Sheila Heti. I was like—oh my gosh. A book is allowed to look like this. I was, like, angry because it was so good and it felt so intimate and real.

How would you personally define poetry?

Poetry is a direct reflection of the crushing pain and exhilarating joy of being alive.

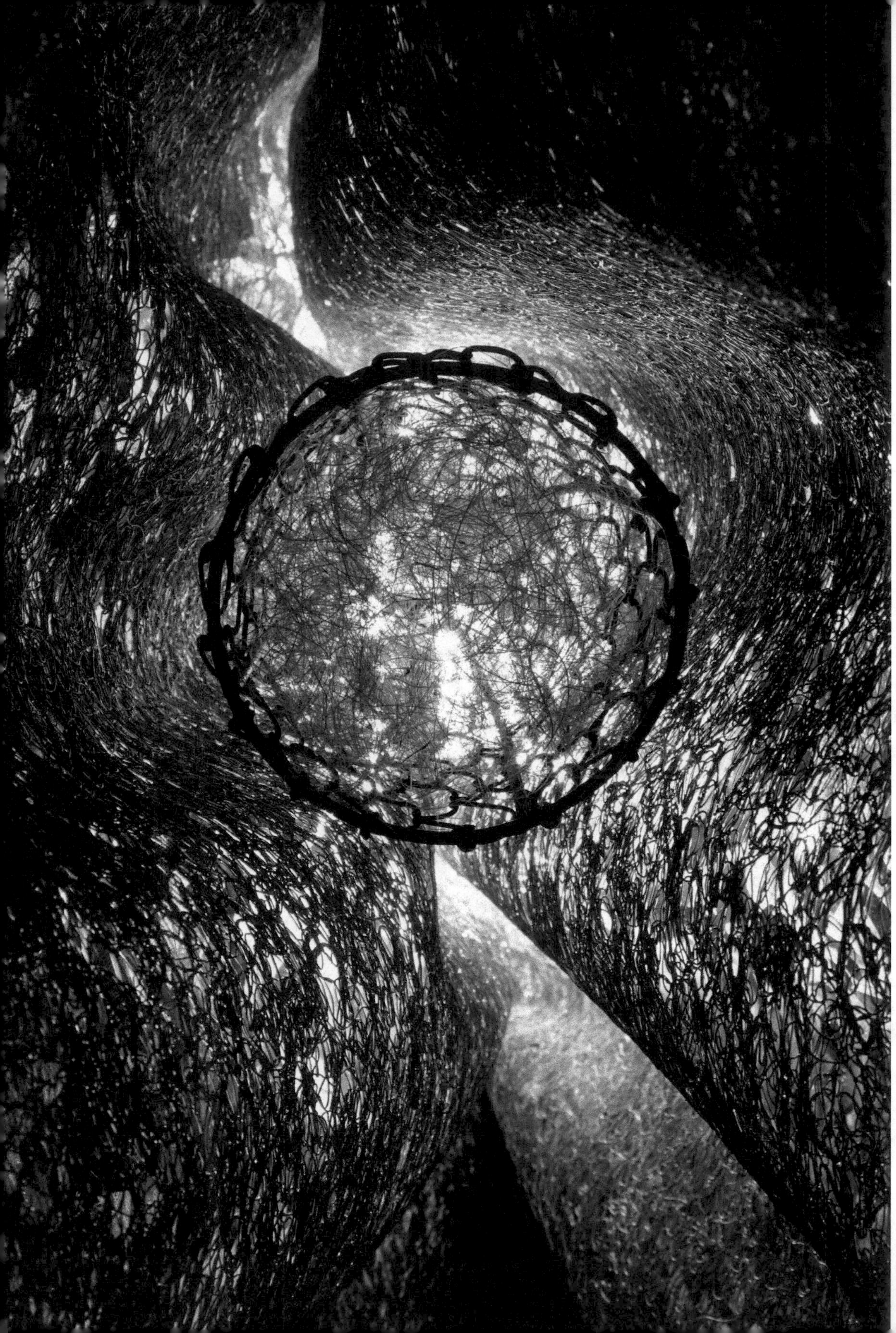

UNTITLED | YI-HUI

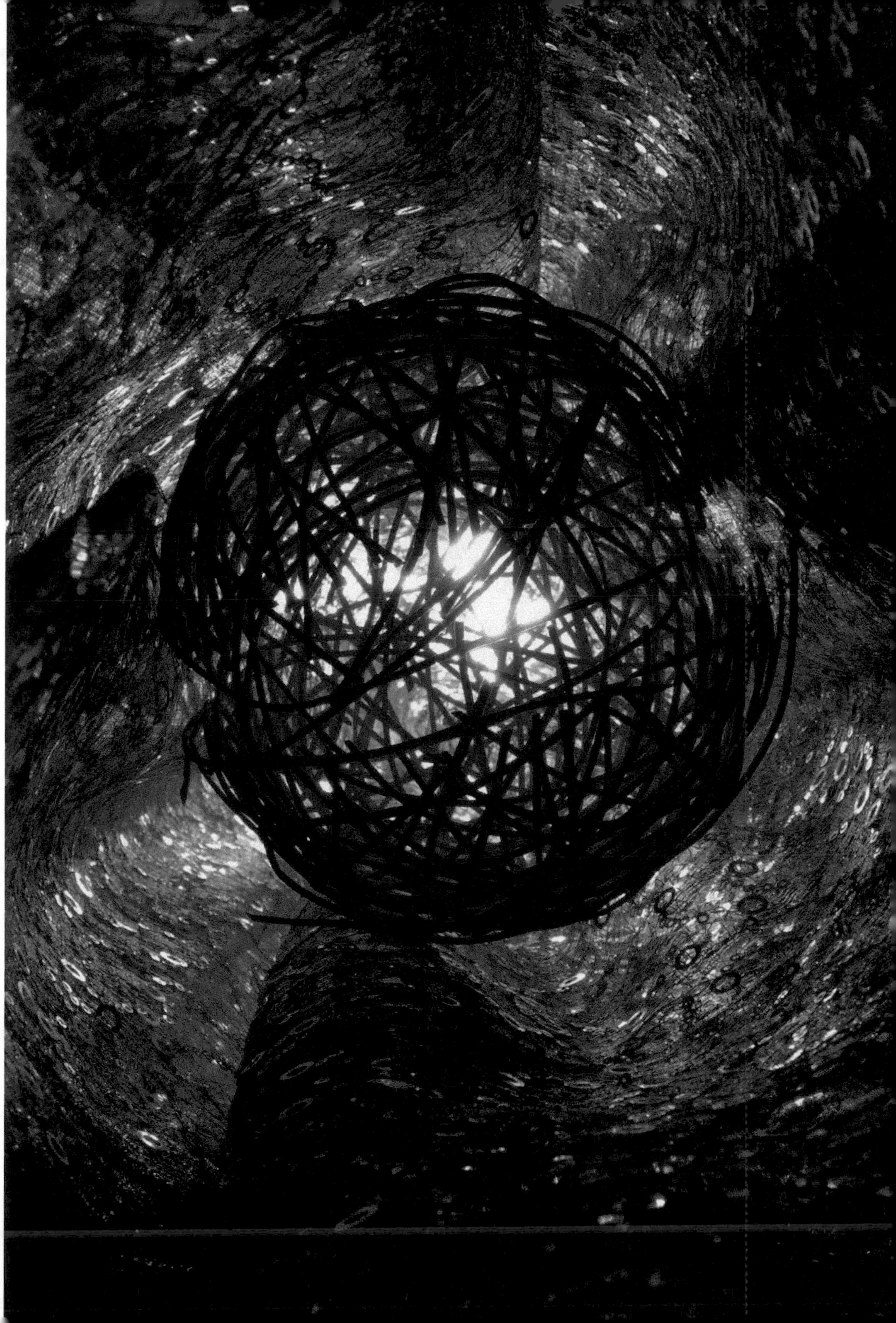

Complexio

(vignettes)

[Narrated by David A——]

—the Three Gorges Dam along the Yangzee River, powerful
enough to slow the Earth's rotation by .06 microseconds daily—

—Armilaria ostoyae may appear to the eye as small mushroom
caps dotting the Malheur National Forest's floor,

but beneath its soil, they form an intricate and interconnected
root system, the single largest organism on planet Earth—

—Overhead, rainforest birds of every color chirp and flit about,
a diverse ecosystem of dialects and complex interactions—

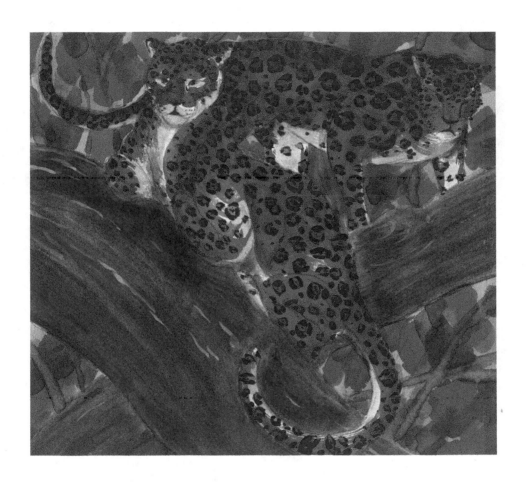

—the jaguar and the leopard. Their difference is minute, an
alteration in the rosette pattern of their camouflaged skins—

—the lions of the isolated Ngorongoro Crater dwindle slowly
through inbreeding. Their pride will pass from the thriving world,
confined to and doomed by this shallow basin—

—biomagnetism of 7.8 billion human beings amounts to drops in the ocean of Earth's magnetic field. Yet even so, scientists have measured noticeable fluctuations in times of great human stress or communalism—

INTERVIEW

When did you create "Complexio"?

The pages were painted in March 2019, but I sketched two thumbnails and a seedling of an idea in a notebook at the end of November 2017 (after a family night walk that reminded me of an impression I'd had from Fourth of July that year).

Do you digitally manipulate photographs? If so, how much did you edit this one?

I tweak colors in Photoshop a little to correct any shift from scanning, but try to keep the artwork as true to the originals as I can.

Is art the medium that you're most invested in?

Art is the vehicle, but storytelling is my core passion. For now, comics is the most expressive form I've invested in, but I don't think it's the only medium I want to utilize or explore.

What is your creative process?

Most stories begin as a synergy point between an image or scene and a bigger human theme that's made me feel strongly in some way. I especially like when the juxtaposition is unexpected or slightly surreal. From there, it's usually building out from those two elements. Lots of notes and dialogue in pocket notebooks. Then half-inch thumbnails, followed by full-size penciled pages, and finally, the rendered artwork in the chosen medium.

There's a certain nonsequitur quality to this comic. Lines are interrupted or start mid-way through, scenes are drastically changed, topics shift—but the thematic content stays fairly consistent. In its roving quality, the piece seems to share much in common with poetry: it expects you to connect the thematic dots between the pages. Could you talk to me about the ideas behind the piece?

Poetry was almost exclusively my artistic output for a decade or so. It's a form I leaned away from when

I started making comics—but over time, it's returned to my visual language. And to your point about the reader having to connect the dots—this has become my favorite aspect of comics. The reader is expected, in large or small ways, to fill in the gaps between panels. It can be as simple as the action from a swinging fist to a crumpling foe, or as complex as placing two superficially unrelated scenes side-by-side and enticing the reader to draw their own emotional or thematic conclusions. We get to paint with empty space. "Complexio" draws that vehicle out, using minute glimpses to lead the reader to a much larger tapestry.

What do you think comics can convey about ecology and environmental issues that differs it from simply writing about the issue?

Building on the previous question, I think comics can present social, political, and environmental issues in ways that are specific and pointed, while also leaving room for a reader to think about and draw their own responses.

Could you talk to us about the materials used to paint this, and some of the difficulties you encountered in doing so?

Watercolors had been my primary medium for a few years, but still they're difficult. There's so little you can do to correct a mistake (but plenty of ways to make it worse), so rendering always feels tense from start to finish.

Your artwork in the comic spans different flora, fauna, and geographies. How did you land on these specific subjects?

Once I had a vague idea of the themes I wanted to explore, it really came down to collecting interesting facts over time. (Having a 4-, 10-, & 18-year-old helps keep this kind of learning continuous in my life.) Deciding which should go into "Complexio" was more instinctual than intellectual to start, then it came down to editing away anything that strayed from the message I was honing.

Could you talk about the formal decisions you've made here? One panel per page with a quote below it. Was this the best way to replicate—in comic form—a David Attenborough narrated tv special?

A great piece of writing advice I've hung onto is to enter a scene as late as possible and get out as soon as you can. With the social and ecological themes I wanted to explore here, that approach seemed like the best way to keep from getting too exact, too heavy-handed—as well as pack the most content into a very limited story. The choice of one panel per page came from both wanting to replicate the experience of watching a nature show, as well as to slow the reader down and focus on a single scene at a time.

What would your advice be to other comic artists trying to write about expansive issues in a shorter form?

Expansive issues should also be personal issues; they're big because they affect so many individuals. I think that finding the universal value of an issue is key, but it can often be presented in very specific minutia. With any short-form storytelling, it's a fine balance between ruthless, intellectual editing down and following your instincts—giving a story room to breathe, to have naturalism and the elements that create emotional tone.

Who are some of your favorite artists? Do you have any recommendations for others who enjoyed your work?

For painted and fine art-centric comics, I would absolutely recommend Manuele Fior's *5,000 Kilometers Per Second* and *Blackbird Days*, Kerascoët and Vehlmann's *Beautiful Darkness*, Kent Williams and Darren Aronofsky's *The Fountain*, Eleanor Davis's *How To Be Happy*, Aidan Koch's *Impressions*, David Prudhomme's *Cruising Through the Louvre*, Richard McGuire's *Here*, & Cyril Pedrosa's *Equinoxes*. We live in such a rich time for comics!

Where can our readers find more of your work? Have you been published before?

Instagram (@json.hart) is my main online presence. I've had comics published in lit mags such as *Black Warrior Review* and the latest issue of *ANMLY*.org, comics and art periodicals like *Ink Brick* and *Illustoria*, comics anthologies, and I've been a previous contributor to *Driftwood Press*.

CONTRIBUTORS

JESSICA HOLBERT is originally from Plymouth Massachusetts and currently resides in Providence Rhode Island with her fiancée. A class of 2015 Bridgewater State University alum, she achieved her Bachelor's of Arts degree with a concentration in writing, studying fiction under professor and author Bruce Machart. Jessica identifies as a transgender woman and feminist. She has previously been published in *America's Emgering Science Fiction & Fantasy Writers* and *America's Emerging Literary Fiction Writers* by *Z Publishing*. Her fiction and poetry has also appeared under her former name James Holbert in magazines such as *Sliver of Stone Magazine, the 2015 Greater Boston Intercollegiate Poetry Festival, Driftwood Press 3.1,* and others. Jessica has received the Best Prose awards in *Volume XI* and *XIV* of *The Bridge*. She is the first fiction writer to have a second story run in *Driftwood Press*.

SETH BRADY TUCKER is founder and co-director of the Longleaf Writers' Conference at Seaside, Florida, and he teaches poetry and fiction workshops at the Lighthouse Writers' Workshop in Denver, is a teaching professor at the Colorado School of Mines, and is the senior prose editor for the *Tupelo Quarterly Review*. He is originally from Wyoming and served as an Army 82nd Airborne Division paratrooper in the Persian Gulf. His second poetry collection, *We Deserve the Gods We Ask For* (2014), won the Gival Press Poetry Award and went on to win post-publication awards including the 2015 Eric Hoffer Book Award. His first book, *Mormon Boy*, won the 2011 Elixir Press Editor's Poetry Prize (published in 2012), and was a Finalist for the 2013 Colorado Book Award. His essays, poetry, and fiction have been published widely in such magazines and journals as *december magazine, Iowa Review, Shenandoah, Poetry Northwest, Verse Daily,* etc.

ANNIE CHRISTAIN is an associate professor of composition and ESOL at SUNY Cobleskill and a former artist resident of the Shanghai Swatch Art Peace Hotel and the Arctic Circle Art and Science Expedition. Her poems have appeared in *Seneca Review, Oxford Poetry, The Chariton Review,* and *The Lifted Brow,* among others. She received the grand prize of the Hart Crane Memorial Poetry Contest, the Greg Grummer Poetry Award, the Oakland School of the Arts Enizagam Poetry Award, and the Neil Shepard Prize in Poetry. *Tall As You Are Tall Between Them,* her debut poetry book, was published in fall 2016 by *C&R Press*.

EMILY PAIGE WILSON is the author of the forthcoming full-length collection *Jalubí* (*Unsolicited Press,* 2022) and two chapbooks: *Hypochondria, Least Powerful of the Greek Gods* (*Glass Poetry Press,* 2020) and *I'll Build Us a Home* (*Finishing Line Press,* 2018). Her work has been nominated for Best New Poets, Best of the Net, and the Pushcart Prize. Connect with her on her website (www.emilypaigewilson.com) and on Twitter (@ Emmy_Golightly).

KAY LIN (Chinese name: Lin Yihuan 林義煥) lives in Singapore. Her poetry has been published by *the december, Live Canon, The Laurel Review, Cloudbank,* and others. Her short story, "night out," was published by *The Tishman Review.* She won the 2019 Open Country Chapbook Prize with her chapbook, *symptoms of the forgotten,* which will be published in the autumn of 2020. She writes in hope of giving words to those whose stories have never been told before.

CHELSEA JACKSON is awestruck by creativity and its power to both challenge and comfort. She uses her poetry to ask hard questions, engage in justice/social change, and explore what it means to be human. Chelsea is published in *Avalon* and *The Platform Review*, and graduated with an MFA in Poetry from Drew University. Originally from Southeastern Virginia, she now lives in Philadelphia with her partner, and their cat and pit bull. You can find her on Twitter and Instagram (@sea_c_j).

JOHN DAVIS JR. is the author of *Hard Inheritance* (*Five Oaks Press*, 2016), *Middle Class American Proverb* (*Negative Capability Press*, 2014), and two other collections of poetry. His poems have appeared in venues such as *Nashville Review, Steel Toe Review, One, The Common online*, and *The American Journal of Poetry*, among many others. He holds an MFA from University of Tampa.

JANIRU LIYANAGE is a fifteen-year-old school student and Pushcart Prize-nominated poet. His recent work appears or is forthcoming in *[PANK], Diode Poetry Journal, Wildness Journal, The Journal Of Compressed Creative Arts, The Ekphrastic Review, Cordite Poetry Review, Homology Lit,* and elsewhere. He is a 2019 winner of the national Dorothea Mackellar Poetry Awards, a recipient of an Ekphrastic Award from *The Ekphrastic Review* and Sydney finalist of the Australian Poetry Slam. Born as the son of Sinhalese immigrants, he currently lives in Sydney.

WREN TUATHA is pursuing her MFA at Goddard College. Her first collection is *Thistle and Brilliant* (*FLP*). Her poetry has appeared in *The Cafe Review, Canary, Sierra Nevada Review, Pirene's Fountain, Lavender Review*, and others. She's editor at *Pitkin Review* and *Califragile*, a journal of climate change and social justice. Wren and partner author/activist C.T. Butler herd rescue goats in the Camp Fire burn zone of California.

TURANDOT SHAYEGAN is a student from Los Angeles, California. She was named a 2019-2020 finalist for the LA Youth Poet Laureate. Her poems seek to deconstruct and disrupt traditional notions of grammar and syntax, exposing the raw materiality of language as a form of new expression. Her work has appeared in *filling Station, Anomaly*, and *Drunk Monkeys*,

amongst others.

JOANNA LEE earned her MD from the Medical College of Virginia in 2007 and a Master's in neuroscience from William & Mary in 2010. Focusing on the intersection of healing and creativity, her poetry has been published in a number of online and print journals and has been nominated for both Best of the Net and Pushcart prizes. *Dissections*, her first chapbook, was published in 2017 (*Finishing Line Press*). Joanna is a founder of the River City Poets community and a co-editor of the recently published anthology, *Lingering in the Margins*. She lives in Richmond, Virginia with her husband John and cat Max.

KATHERINE FALLON's poems have appeared in *AGNI, Juked, Apple Valley Review, Colorado Review, Meridian, Foundry*, and *Best New Poets 2019*, among others. Her chapbook, *The Toothmaker's Daughters*, is available through *Finishing Line Press*. She reads for *[PANK]*, assists in editing *Terrible Orange Review*, and is a 2020 AWP Writer to Writer Mentee. She shares domestic square footage with two cats and her favorite human, who helps her zip her dresses.

MADELEINE FRANK is a recent graduate of St. Lawrence University where she studied geology and creative writing. During her time there, she served as the head editor of poetry for the school's literary magazine, *The Laurentian Magazine*. Since graduating, she has worked in college admissions and scientific writing. This fall she will move from her hometown of Rochester, New York to St. Louis, Missouri to begin her MFA in creative writing (nonfiction) at Washington University in St. Louis.

MOLLY OBERSTEIN-ALLEN is a writer living in Kansas City, Missouri. She loves public transportation, running outside, and reading books. Her work has appeared in gracious publications including *Spy Kids Review* and *Maudlin House*. You can find her on Twitter (@hiitsmolly).

COZ FRIMPONG is a muddy watercolor illustrator based in New Jersey. You can keep up with the mess on instagram (@evzosart).

GEOFFREY DETRANI is an artist and writer. His artwork has been exhibited widely and he is the recipient of numerous grants and fellowships. His poetry has appeared in numerous journals and literary magazines. More about his work can be found on his website (www.geoffreydetrani.com).

YI-HUI HUANG is a professor of Digital Media Technologies at East Stroudsburg University, Pennsylvania. She has an MFA in photography from the University of Iowa and a PhD in Art Education from Ohio State University. Her photographic work expresses emotions concerning her immigration experiences.

AIMEE COZZA is a freelance illustrator out of New England. She graduated from the New Hampshire Institute of Art in 2012 with a bachelor's degree in illustration. Aimee primary creates digital dark-beautiful illustrations based on the surreal and unsettling. Her most common subjects are space, extraterrestrial worlds, fantastical beings, creatures, and ominous, off-putting subjects. She explores themes such as duality, disconnection, doomed romance, perception of space and time, mental illnesses often not spoken of, trauma, and the uphill battle against stereotypes. She also is an aspiring writer and is co-author of a forthcoming three part book series.

JASON HART is a visual storyteller based in Dayton, Ohio. His narrative works have appeared in *Black Warrior Review, ANMLY, Illustoria, Ink Brick*, and elsewhere.

CPSIA information can be obtained
at www.ICGtesting.com
Printed in the USA
FSHW011234170820

9 781949 065077